A GUIDE TO
WILD FRUITS
OF BORNEO

A GUIDE TO
WILD FRUITS
OF BORNEO

Anthony Lamb

Natural History Publications (Borneo)
Kota Kinabalu

2019

Published by

Natural History Publications (Borneo) Sdn. Bhd. (216807-X)
A913, 9th Floor, Wisma Merdeka Phase 1,
P.O. Box 15566,
88864 Kota Kinabalu, Sabah, Malaysia.
Tel: +6088-233098   Fax: +6088-240768
e-mail: info@nhpborneo.com
Website: www.nhpborneo.com

A Guide to Wild Fruits of Borneo
by Anthony Lamb
Edited by Louise Neo and Kay Lyons

ISBN 978-983-812-191-0

First published April 2019.

Half-title page: Tarap (*Artocarpus odoratissimus*).
    Photo: Roslan bin Lusi.
Frontispiece: A selection of wild fruits and seeds.
Photo: Chien Lee.
Title page: *Durio crassipes*. Photo: A. Lamb.
Page v: The canopy of the mixed lowland dipterocarp
    foresrt. Photo: Chien Lee.
Above: *Artocarpus lanceifolius* ssp. *clementis*.
    Photo: A. Lamb.
Opposite Foreword: A large male orangutan with figs.
    Photo: Guy Broome.
Page ix: *Nephelium lappaceum*. Photo: A. Phillipps.

Printed in Taiwan.

Contents

CONTENTS

A Guide to Wild Fruits of Borneo

CONTENTS

Foreword

It is amazing to think that there could be nearly 500 species of native plants that yield edible fruit, nuts and seeds in the forests of Borneo alone. Research has indicated that over 15,000 plant species could exist in Borneo, nearly 10,000 of which are found in the lowland mixed dipterocarp forests. This is where the highest diversity of edible fruit trees and their wild relatives resides, including mangoes, durians, mangosteens, jackfruit, and rambutans.

With landscapes going through drastic changes, some irreversibly so, concern for loss of genetic resources from our wild stocks is very real. When so many species exist within the intricate ecological environment of rain forests, it is not surprising that our flora and fauna stock-taking goes slowly. Many reasons delay faster documentation, most importantly a lack of trained professionals and specialists to study this enormous diversity. But the intrinsic richness of rain forests itself is fascinating, although when tracts of forestland come under threat and degradation, this also means that the diversity is imperilled. With Borneo's wild fruits coming from such diverse plant families, the botanical effort will have to be much increased.

We have lost much of Borneo's forest resources, due to factors such as landuse transformation and repeated catastrophic fires. Perhaps ironically, another serious loss is accelerated through the availability of good-tasting and high-yielding clones that have become so popular that they have displaced many of the more traditionally grown relatives or clones. Older clones are ignored and disposed of, and little planted anymore, with the consequence that a traditionally gathered set of genetic materials has gone to waste. In fact, wild relatives represent an important genetic resource with which to breed or select variant forms with particular useful attributes. Wild rambutan trees growing on nutrient-poor kerangas soils, for example, should be ideal for grafting rootstock, if not breeding improvement, of select varieties to grow in less fertile substrates. When the forest is depleted or gone, the options will begin to run out.

A book like the present one, which presents 109 species of edible fruit found in 34 families, is a beginning step in the right direction. It is hoped that with such a guide, awareness and interest in the relevance of wild genetic resources will step up. With greater curiosity, documentation and study, the importance of this fruit-plant resource comes into sharper focus. Some rare species have been included to allow awareness of differences in species attributes, both in form and how they exist or survive.

It would be truly fruitful if the people of Borneo and beyond with an interest in fruits and options for new cultivars find this publication useful. There may even be candidates for new fruit varieties and oil-rich seeds to give new economic alternatives. I am very proud that the author, Datuk Anthony Lamb, and the principal of Natural History Publications (Borneo), Datuk C.L. Chan, have produced such an appealing, practical and informative account that introduces the fascinating world of forest fruits.

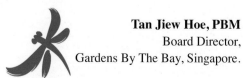

Tan Jiew Hoe, PBM
Board Director,
Gardens By The Bay, Singapore.

BORNEO

- ◎ Capital
- ◉ Important City
- ○ Small city or town
- ✈ International airport
- ● Other place of interest
- ▮ Parks and reserves

metres	feet
9000	3000
6000	2000
4500	1500
3000	1000
1200	400
600	200
0	0

0 — 100 km

0 — 50 miles

Layang-Layang Island

Pulau Banggi Island

Su lu Sea

SOUTH CHINA SEA

Kudat

Kota Belud

Kinabalu Park

Tuaran

Kota Kinabalu

Crocker Range National Park

Papar

Sepilok Wildlife Reserve

Sandakan

Kinabatangan Wildlife Sanctu...

Gomantong Caves

Tambunan

Kinabatangan

Tenom

SABAH

Danum Valley

Tabin Wild Reserve

Bandar Seri Begawan

Lahad Datu

Labuan Island

BRUNEI

Ulu Temburong National Park

Maliau Basin

Miri

Tawau

Sempor...

Lambir Hills National Park

Mabul

Kapal...

Niah Caves National Park

Mulu Caves

Sipadan Isl...

Similajau National Park

Niah Caves

Gunung Mulu National Park

Bintulu

Bario

Tarakan

Cele b Sea

MALAYSIA

Kayan Mentarang National Park

SARAWAK

Rejang

Sibu

Kapit

EAST KALIMANTAN

Damai

Bako National Park

Kubah National Park

Matang

Batang Ai National Park

Sangkulirang

Gunung Gading National Park

Kuching

Betung Karimun National Park

WEST KALIMANTAN

Kapuas

INDONESIA

Pontianak

Kutai National Park

Bukit Baka National Park

Melawi

Samarinda

CENTRAL KALIMANTAN

Gunung Palung National Park

Katingan

Kapuas

Balikpapan

Ketapang

Sampit

Palangkaraya

Barito

MAKASSAR STRAIT

Sukamara

Sampit

SOUTH KALIMANTAN

Tanjung Puting National Park

Banjarmasin

JAVA SEA

Map of Borneo.

Introduction

The island of Borneo is the third largest in the world after Greenland and New Guinea, with an area of 737,000 sq. km. Kalimantan, at 539,460 sq. km (c. 72% of Borneo), is part of Indonesia and now consists of five provinces (i.e., North, East, South, Central and West Kalimantan). Sabah, at 73,619 sq. km (c. 10%), is part of Malaysia and covers the northern portion of Borneo. Sarawak, at 124,450 sq. km (c. 17%), is also part of Malaysia and covers the north-western side of the island. Brunei on the west coast of Borneo occupies 5765 sq. km, just under 1% of Borneo. The island straddles the equator, with the northern tip in Sabah reaching 7°N and the southern extremity of Kalimantan reaching 4°S.

Biogeographically, like most of Sumatra, West Java and Peninsular Malaysia, Borneo is part of tropical Asia, with tropical evergreen forest in an ever-wet climate. Only a small area of N.E. Sabah & S.E. Kalimantan has recorded long dry seasons.

Borneo is also part of Malesia, a botanical region that includes the Malay Peninsula, the islands of Indonesia through to New Guinea, Singapore, the Philippines, and East Timor. This floristic region refers to plant distribution, and has no special relevance to fauna. Borneo is considered to be one of the top five biodiversity hotspots in the world and the Mount Kinabalu area in Sabah, with over 5500 plant species in an area of just 120 sq. km, is quite possibly the richest plant diversity hotspot worldwide (van der Ent 2013).

Some of the plant species in Borneo have a much wider distribution, some even occurring in mainland tropical Asia, including southern India, tropical Africa, and the neotropical regions of South and Central America. Others, however, have more narrow distributions, with a number completely restricted (endemic) to Borneo itself.

In this guide, we have tried to include a rough idea of the distribution of the species covered and indicate which species are endemic to the island, with notes on the number of species and centres of diversity for a particular genus or family.

In preparing this guide, it was necessary to identify the most important or interesting plant species that produce edible fruits, nuts, and seeds for human consumption, especially those better known to the local indigenous tribes who have inhabited Borneo for several centuries. This is a pictorial guide to the fruits, and gives the latest botanical names of the different species and their affiliation. Most species only fruit seasonally, and some only once in several

An orangutan feeding on *Artocarpus anisophyllus*.

years, depending on climatic conditions or events. It should be remembered that identification of particular trees, shrubs or herbs without flowers or fruits can be difficult, so we endeavour to mention vegetative characters where potentially helpful. An illustrated glossary of botanical terms is provided to help with understanding various characters and terms.

Historical Aspects

This guide covers only some of the many native edible fruits, nuts and seeds, that in the past were consumed by local inhabitants, who in earliest times mainly lived along the coasts, before subsequently moving up the major rivers, and finally also into the hills and mountain regions of Borneo.

During this earlier period, migrants may have introduced crop plants, fruits and nuts, but these early settlers would have quickly identified and utilised the huge diversity of native species, especially during foraging and hunting trips into the forests. Of course, they also harvested other forest products for trading, such as edible bird nests, beeswax, damar or resins, and rattans. Inevitably, they brought back various edible fruits and nuts that were more important for consumption for planting in their villages. They also learnt which of these had to be processed, such as through boiling or roasting, before being consumed.

With the increasing population came road access, the introduction of economic plantation crops such as coconuts, followed later by rubber and pepper, markets and international trade, and the development and the introduction of many more improved varieties of fruits and nuts. This has led many communities to no longer consume some of the local species, in favour of the sweeter, juicier selected varieties of fruits such as mangoes and rambutans, and introduced fruits such as oranges.

Past generations probably depended on and utilised a diverse variety of wild fruits and nuts in the range of nearly 500 species, so that many such species have great potential to be developed in breeding and selection programmes, including those that could help enhance the resistance of cultivated stock to pests and diseases. Some species have become quite rare, being dramatically reduced through loss of their forest habitats to land-clearing for agriculture.

The Agricultural Departments have to some extent selected and established collections of some of the promising species in stations in all the Bornean territories, but they cover a very small proportion of the total diversity, especially the rare species. This guide covers one or two of these rare species to illustrate the overall need to conserve these species especially where their habitat is threatened. The conservation of germplasm on a larger scale is now getting more urgent in view of the increasing loss of forest land to development, especially by plantation crops, particularly in the evergreen lowland mixed dipterocarp forest where plant diversity is often highest.

Some species have also been reduced by inappropriate harvesting. If one has been in forests during a good fruiting season, the variation in fruit quality is surprising with a single species of wild rambutan varying from very sour to sweet, and of course, as soon as the fruit are ripe the wildlife devours them in a very short time. Many villagers have told me that they remember their fathers bringing sacks of these sweet fruits back to the village, but as the tree was tall and difficult to harvest, they usually chopped it down for ease of harvesting. The result was that many of the sweeter varieties have disappeared, except

A Guide to Wild Fruits of Borneo

those planted around the villages. Similarly, during the 1970s and 1980s in Sabah, during the timber boom, I used to visit certain wild durian or mango species when I thought the fruit would be ripe, only to find the whole tree gone, harvested for both its timber and fruit by the logging company, even though harvesting of wild fruit trees was forbidden by the Forestry Department.

The forest industry in Borneo is now practising sustainable forest management, especially in the State of Sabah, in logged over forest, or those affected by forest fires in the past, for instance. This includes enrichment planting of species, mainly trees, to maintain the diversity of species that also provide sources of food such as fruits and seeds, on which the wildlife depend.

In this respect it can be difficult to obtain seeds from the natural forest, since ripe fruits are very quickly consumed by the wildlife. So the germplasm collections in the Agricultural Stations, as previously mentioned, could be a very important source of seeds for the enrichment planting programmes, but they have only been utilised to a small extent.

Today, many of those wild fruit trees originally planted around villages in Borneo have been replaced by the latest and sweetest mango or durian clones, due to the lack of land around the village. This results in a huge loss of the original native germplasm that could have been used for future selection programmes, as the plant breeder needs a wide range of plants (genetic material) from different localities and forest types from which to make his selections for crossing, in order to make improved varieties available.

Borneo's tropical evergreen rainforests are considered among the most species-rich in the world with a possible 15,000 species in over 300 families. The endemicity is not known for certain, but could include nearly 5000 (30%) or more endemic species. The evergreen lowland mixed Dipterocarp forests in Borneo are considered the richest, having a total of nearly 10,000 plant species, with over 2000 tree species, and are the most extensive in terms of coverage of the land mass of Borneo (Ashton 1982 & 2004).

Meijaard & Shiel (2013) highlighted that in 1973, 75.7% (558,060 sq. km) of Borneo was forested, but that by 2010, this had decreased by 30% (168,493 sq. km), with the highest losses being recorded in Sabah at 39% and Kalimantan at 30%, and much lower for Brunei and Sarawak. This was due to large areas being converted to plantations of mainly oil palms. So in 2010, 52.9% (389,567 sq. km) remained as forest, of which 209,649 sq. km was still unlogged. Also, a major El Niño drought event in 1982–1983 over a period of 6 months resulted in large forest fires in both Sabah and Kalimantan, both in logged lowland forest and peatswamp forest areas, which contributed a lot to this forest loss (Beaman et al. 1985).

This huge loss of lowland forests, with its high diversity of native edible fruits and nuts that are mainly tree species, has meant a significant reduction in the overall germplasm pool of these species and consequently a reduced potential of finding better cultivars for breeding work. It has to be noted, however, that the remaining intact logged forest still retains a high diversity of tree species that have conservation value, and many of these forests are being managed, and improved, with enrichment planting.

Types of tropical rainforest in Borneo

It is impossible in this guide to document all of the many types of forests in Borneo, due to a wide range of geological features, soils, altitudinal zones, and climatic factors, that influence the composition and structure of each forest zone.

The following are the main forest types found in Borneo with the altitudinal range at which they occur:

1. Seashore and Coastal Forest on the mainland and offshore islands (0–30 m)
2. Coastal and Estuarine Mangrove & Swamp Forests (0–30 m)
3. Peatswamp Forests (0–50 m)
4. Mixed Lowland Dipterocarp & Riverine Forest (0–300 m)
5. Mixed Hill & Riverine Dipterocarp Forest (300–800 m)
6. Upper Hill Mixed Dipterocarp Forest (800–1200 m)
7. Lower Montane Forest (1200–1800 m)
8. Upper Montane Forest (1800–2200 m)
9. Heath Forests (kerangas) – Lowland, Hill & Montane
10. Limestone Forest – Coastal & Hill
11. Forest on ultramafic soils (Lowland to Lower Montane)

The main forest formations or types are covered in much greater detail by Whitmore (1984) in *Tropical Rain Forests of the Far East*, Payne (2010) in *Wild Sabah*, and by Ashton (1995) in his Biogeography and Ecology chapter in Volume 1 of the *Tree Flora of Sabah and Sarawak*. The different forest types are also well illustrated and covered for particular areas, and show the effects of soils, climate and geology on the make-up of forest structure and flora, in detailed volumes on *Danum Valley, The Rain Forest* (2012), and *Maliau*

Basin, Sabah's Lost World, both by Hans P. Hazebroek, Tengku Zainal Adlin & Waidi Sinun, and similarly by Hans P. Hazebroek & Morshidi (2000) in the *National Parks of Sarawak*. Another useful reference that covers some of the edible fruits is Christensen (2002), *Ethnobotany of the Iban and the Kelabit*. Publications that directly cover and illustrate the edible fruits and nuts that must be mentioned are *Wild Fruits and Vegetables in Sarawak* (2nd edition 1988), the *Indigenous Fruits of Sarawak* (2003) and *Edible Wild Plants in Sarawak* (2013). *Brunei Darussalam Fruits in Colour* (1992) and, for Sabah, *Fruits of Sabah* Vol. 1 (2007) and *Fruits, Nuts and Spices* (1993) cover many, but not all the fruits of Brunei and Sabah. Some of the fruits and nuts of Kalimantan and Indonesia are covered in *Potret Buah Nusantara* (2016).

In this guide, we will mention some of the species of edible fruits found in the different forest types.

1. *Seashore and Coastal Forest on the Mainland and Offshore Islands*

Along the coast of Borneo not occupied by mangroves, and in estuarine vegetation, there are stretches of sandy beaches often fringed with a narrow belt of vegetation, made up of plant species that have adapted to tolerate incoming storms with strong winds and salt spray, behind which are other forest types on different soils. This vegetation consists of tree species such as *Terminalia catappa* (Combretaceae) with fruits with nuts with edible kernels, and trees such as *Calophyllum inophyllum* (penaga laut) and *Pongamia pinnata*, whose seeds produce a non-edible oil used for fuel, and smaller shrubby treelets such as the seashore hibiscus (now *Talipariti tiliaceum*) and *Morinda citrifolia* (Rubiaceae); the last also has edible fruits. *Pandanus odoratissimus* (Pandanaceae), the seashore screw pine, has edible but fibrous fruits in Borneo, so is rarely eaten, but selected varieties are widely cultivated. The fruits are consumed in the Pacific Islands, however the leaves are commonly utilised for weaving. Behind this seashore belt we can also find *Garcinia hombroniana,* the seashore mangosteen with edible fruits, and the shrub *Rhodomyrtus tomentosa* (Myrtaceae), whose small purple fruits are popular as a relish with children in coastal settlements. More rarely, we find large trees of *Sterculia foetida* (Malvaceae) with edible seeds and, for Sabah, the rare seashore mango *Mangifera pentandra* (Anacardiaceae), the plum mango or *mangga telur*. Many of these species are also found on the more rocky coastlines that tolerate similar windy, and salty conditions.

2. *Coastal and Estuarine Mangrove and Swamp Forest*

Borneo has many rivers flowing to the coasts all around the island, many forming large estuaries formed from the silt and mud brought down by the rivers. These mudflats have developed three main forest zones. The first is the coastal mangrove forest, that has developed in tidal areas, and that can extend quite far up the low-lying areas affected by tidal saline waters.

Very few species have edible fruits, an exception being *Sonneratia caseolaris* (Lythraceae).

The second forest formation found on these mudflats, where, at low tides, fresh water flows into the areas, is the extensive, impenetrable palm swamp forests that can cover very large areas in the estuarine deltas and extend quite far up the rivers where the banks are still affected by the tides. This swamp forest is dominated by a single species of palm, *Nypa fruticans* (Arecaceae), that is utilised for roof thatching, using the palm fronds, for nectar from the inflorescence to produce palm sugar and alcohol, and for the edible kernels of the young fruits.

The less extensive third zone is the mudflats behind or between the mangrove or nipah swamp forests, largely inundated with fresh or brackish water (not salt water) and often dominated by stands of thorny nibong palms,

Coastal forest

Oncosperma tigillarium (Arecaceae) mixed with other trees and palms. A few edible fruit species are found in this zone, such as a little-known *Pandanus* species and *Sandoricum borneense* (Meliaceae).

3. *Peatswamp Forests*

These forests have largely developed over marine alluvium near the coast that was formerly mangrove forests but which dried out as river deltas moved further out to sea over time. The salty marine clays high in sulphur, together with poor drainage and acidic conditions, have led to the development of peat.

In river deltas, mixed with patches of fresh water swamp forest, and in larger river basins and flood plains, the peat is not very deep and some wild edible fruit species occur, such as *Garcinia* (Clusiaceae) species, *Xanthophyllum* (Polygalaceae) species, and rarely *Bouea oppositifolia* (Anacardiaceae) and *Sarcotheca diversifolia* (Oxalidaceae). *Eleiodoxa conferta* (Arecaceae) also has edible fruits.

The other peatswamp forest type, which is common in coastal and inland delta areas from Brunei, through Sarawak to West Kalimantan, has peat up to 20 m deep. Here, tree species such as *Mangifera havilandii* (Anacardiaceae) have edible fruits. Other understorey trees with edible fruits that have been recorded are *Xanthophyllum stipitatum* (Polygalaceae), *Nephelium maingayi*, *Pometia pinnata* (Sapindaceae), *Garcinia rostrata* (Clusiaceae) and *Alangium havilandii* (Cornaceae). Logging and El Niño events with long droughts have led to huge areas of these peatswamp forests being destroyed by forest fires, leaving a degraded forest often of open vegetation of grasses and sedges, or stunted secondary forest.

Peatswamp forests

A Guide to Wild Fruits of Borneo

Peatswamp forests

4. *Mixed Lowland Dipterocarp and Riverine Forest*

Overall these are the richest forests in terms of diversity of flora and fauna, and contain many plant species with fruits and nuts (or seeds) edible to humans. Their conversion to plantations has meant a huge loss of diverse germplasm.

The forest on the richer clay soils is characterised by tall emergents reaching heights of 60–80 m. Dipterocarp species dominate. However, other emergents are commonly found such as *Koompassia excelsa* (*menggaris*), *Octomeles sumatrana* (*binuang*) and a few with edible nuts such as *Dialium indum* (*keranji*) and *Parkia speciosa* (*petai*) in the Fabaceae.

Below these emergent trees, within the main forest canopy, are families with many species of edible fruits. In the Dipterocarpaceae we find species with large edible seeds called illipe nuts, such as *Shorea macrophylla* and *S. splendida*. Along with other dipterocarp species they usually fruit every few years in a 'mast' fruiting, the nuts producing edible oil, used in cooking, but also exported to be used as a substitute for cocoa butter. In the Moraceae *Artocarpus anisophyllus* (*terap ikal*), *A. tamaran* (*tamaran*), *A. teysmannii*

Mixed dipterocarp forest

(*cempedak air*), *A. elasticus* (*terap*) and *A. sericicarpus* (*terap bulu*) are main canopy trees, with several other edible species in the genus as understorey trees. Burseraceae includes three species with edible nuts in the main canopy, *Canarium megalanthum* (*meritus*), *C. decumanum* (*kenari sabrang*) and *Dacryodes rostrata* (*kedondong*). Another main canopy tree with edible seeds is *Elateriospermum tapos* (*perah*) in the Euphorbiaceae which is more common in mixed dipterocarp forest on hilly terrain.

In the Anacardiaceae there are a large number of wild mango species reaching the main canopy, such as *Mangifera applanata* (*lumpingas*), *M. caesia* (*beluno*), *M. decandra* (*binjai hutan*), *M. griffithii* (*rawa* or *bahab*), *M. macrocarpa* (*mangga hutan*), *M. quadrifida* (*rawa*), and *M. torquenda* (*lamantan*). However, these species are now very rare as most of their habitat has been lost.

On the richer clay soils, two durian species are common main canopy trees, *Durio graveolens* (*durian merah*) and *D. zibethinus* (*durian putih*) in the Malvaceae, also the widespread *Scorodocarpus borneensis* (*bawang hutan*) in the Olacaceae and *Castanopsis megacarpa* (*berangan*) in Fagaceae, both with edible seeds.

Below the main canopy is a whole range of shade-tolerant understorey tree species and climbers, that often become more common along the river banks, where extra light allows them to fruit more often. Here are found the largest number of species with edible fruits in any forest formation. To give an idea of this diversity, the following are some of the species which are listed in the different families, some of which are covered in this guide.

Pangium edule (*kepayang*), Achariaceae, *Alangium javanicum* (*kondolon*), Cornaceae, *Mangifera casturi* (*mangga kasturi*) in Kalimantan, *M. foetida* (*bacang*) and *M. pajang* (*bambangan*), which is endemic to Borneo, in the family Anacardiaceae. *M. pajang,* with four reported varieties, has fruits which are utilised by a local company to make jams and juices.

The woody climbers *Uvaria grandiflora* (*pisang-pisang*) in the Annonaceae, and *Willughbeia* species in the Apocynaceae such as *W. angustifolia*, *W. coriacea* and *W. sarawacensis*, often referred to as *serapit* or *kubal*.

Climbing rattan palms in Arecaceae, many with edible fruits that are eaten by forest gatherers collecting the long rattan stems (canes) for furniture and mats. Other edible rattan species in several genera are found, such as *Calamus*, *Daemonorops* and *Korthalsia*.

Understorey trees, such as the kepel apple, *Stelechocarpus burahol* (*kepel*) in the Annonaceae, that is cultivated in Java and Sumatra. *Canarium*

Riverine forest

odontophyllum (*kembayau* or *dabai*), the popular tropical olive in the Burseraceae, is also widely cultivated.

Over 50 species of wild mangosteens, *Garcinia* species in the family Clusiaceae, have been recorded for Borneo, and many are understorey lowland to hill species in mixed dipterocarp forest, that have edible fruit, including the 'Queen of Fruits' *G. mangostana*. Several have a sweet edible arillode (fruit pulp), but many are sour and utilised in cooking with fish in particular. Among the other wild mangosteens utilised are *Garcinia nervosa* (*kandis gajah*), *G. nitida* (*kandis hutan*), *G. forbesii* (rose kandis or Brunei cherry) and *G. parvifolia* (*kandis*).

Other smaller understorey trees, such as *Flacourtia rukum* (*rukam*) in the Salicaceae, which is commonly cultivated and utilised in making jams and jellies, and species of *Antidesma* with very small fruits in the family Phyllanthaceae, are also eaten by hunters when trekking through these forests.

Durio testudinarum (the tortoise durian or *durian kura*, Malvaceae), with its fruit borne on the bole or tree trunk, is a spectacle, and is widespread both on sandy and clay soils. Understorey trees that extend from the lowland mixed forest into the hill forest include several species in the genera *Artocarpus* and *Ficus* in the Moraceae, including *Ficus callosa*, found only in Sabah, and *F. nota*. In *Artocarpus* there are several species of which *A. odoratissimus* (*tarap*) and *A. integer* (*cempedak*) are very popular, and cultivated, fruit trees. Others include *A. dadah* (*dadah*), *A. lanceifolius* (*keledang*), *A. limpato* (*kesusu*) and *A. rigidus* (*periam*), the last three having delicious fruits.

Another family, Phyllanthaceae, also has many understorey trees with edible fruits, of which some are cultivated and the fruits sold in the markets, generally referred to as *tampoi*. In cultivated species, *Baccaurea angulata* (*belimbing hutan*), *B. bracteata* (*tampoi payu*), *B. macrocarpa* (*tampoi putih*) and *B. motleyana* (*rambai*) are the most common and widespread. *B. lanceolata* (*limpaung*), *B. polyneura* (*jentik jentik*) and *B. tetandra* (*kunau*) are some of the other edible species in lowland and hill mixed dipterocarp forest.

Baccaurea species generally start fruiting 4–6 years after planting, the fruits being berries or fleshy capsules with an edible arillode covering the seed. One possible reason for them not being commonly in cultivation is that for many species 70–90% of seeds planted have turned out to be male trees, so that they do not produce fruits and farmers often chop them down. Of course, if female trees have no nearby male trees, they can produce fruits, but with no seeds and edible arillode. Female trees could be propagated by budgrafting seedlings or marcotting female trees as has been successfully practised with other species.

Baccaurea species are very important sources of food for wildlife in Bornean forests because, like figs, they fruit regularly outside the main fruiting season when other fruits are scarce.

Amongst the most popular edible fruits are the rambutans and longans in the large family Sapindaceae, with a large number of species found as understorey trees or in riverine forest. The rare and little known *Glenniea philippinensis* occurs in the low hills of Sabah, and small understorey trees of *Lepisanthes alata* (*engkilili*) and *L. multijuga* are found in lowland riverine and hill forest to 300 m; the former is cultivated in Brunei and Sarawak. The common and widespread lowland species *Pometia pinnata* (*kasai*) is also common along river banks. More popular and widely cultivated are the longans or *mata kucing* ('cat's eyes') with *Dimocarpus longan* ssp. *malesianus* found in Borneo, as is its lesser known spiny variety var. *echinatus*. *Dimocarpus dentatus* and *D. fumatus* (*mata kucing hutan*) are generally gathered in the forest. These are all understorey trees below 30 m in height that also occur along river banks.

Nephelium cuspidatum (*rambutan hutan*) with a sour to sweet juicy sarcotesta (fruit pulp) is widespread with several varieties recorded, with the large-fruited juicy var. *robustum* being cultivated in villages. *N. lappaceum*, the true rambutan, is one of the most popular and widely cultivated tropical fruits with many selected clones available. Three wild varieties for Borneo are recognised. *N. maingayi* (*serait*) and *N. melanomiscum* (*mertapang*) are sometimes cultivated, whereas the popular *N. ramboutan-ake* (*pulasan*, *meritam*) has many sweet and juicy selected varieties.

Other understorey trees that are also commonly cultivated are *Sandoricum koetjape* (*sentul*) and *Lansium domesticum* (*langsat*) in the Meliaceae, also *Litsea garciae* (*engkala*) in the Lauraceae.

Not so common in the Meliaceae are *Sandoricum borneense* (*kelampu*) and *Walsura pinnata* (*lantupak*). Proteaceae includes *Heliciopsis artocarpoides* (*kurungguor putat*), and in Polygalaceae, *Xanthophyllum stipitatum* (*langgir*), which are rarely, if ever, cultivated.

This large number of understorey trees with edible fruits further illustrates the great diversity of species in the lowland mixed dipterocarp forest, of which many species also extend into the hill forest above 300 m.

Finally we come to the shrubs and treelets on the forest floor, which can be dealt with together with the herbs.

In the Arecaceae there are several species of a clumping palm in the genus *Salacca* with edible fruits of which *S. affinis* (*salak hutan*) is sometimes cultivated and fruits sold in the markets.

The giant herbs include several species of wild banana in the Musaceae. Most have edible fruits full of seeds, such as *M. acuminata*, but since this species has produced many cultivars, from a hybrid that is seedless, and which are easy to cultivate, these wild species are seldom eaten.

The family Zingiberaceae has many species of wild gingers with edible fruits, eaten by hunters and gatherers on their trips into the forest. Those genera with species that are consumed include *Alpinia, Amomum, Etlingera, Hornstedtia* and *Plagiostachys*.

Another fruit often consumed is from the herb *Molineria latifolia* (*tembuka*) in the family Hypoxidaceae.

A very important variant of the lowland forest is the riparian or riverine forest along the banks of the larger streams and rivers. Here, the red river fig *Ficus racemosa* (*tangkol*) in the Moraceae, *Sandoricum borneense* (*sentul hutan*) in the Meliaceae, and *Dillenia indica* (elephant apple) in the Dilleniaceae, all have edible fruits; other fruit trees on these river banks include *Dimocarpus fumatus* and *Pometia pinnata* (*kasai*) in the Sapindaceae,

Dracontomelon dao (*seronsob*) and *Pentaspadon motleyi* (*pelajau*) with its water-borne fruits in the Anacardiaceae, and *Microcos crassifolia* (*chanderai*) in the Malvaceae.

5. *Mixed Hill and Riverine Dipterocarp Forest*

This formation also covers a large part of the land area of Borneo as it includes most of Borneo's Central Range that is now included in the 'Heart of Borneo'. This project, jointly agreed upon by all the countries of Borneo, is now largely made up of totally protected forest areas with connecting corridors, or are adjacent areas along the international boundaries between the countries. The main purpose is to protect water resources from these mountain ranges, and at the same time conserve the very diverse flora and fauna. However, large areas of this hilly terrain, in all the countries apart from Brunei, have been inhabited by hill tribes over many generations and cleared of forest in shifting agricultural practices. These hill forests have also been important sources of wild meat and other forest products, including wild fruits and nuts.

The terrain in this formation includes mostly ridge forest, with steep forested slopes. There are a large number of species in the Fagaceae (oaks and chestnuts) and species in families such as the Lauraceae here.

Many of the tree species with edible fruits and nuts found in lowland forest start to decrease with altitude, but a large number do occur right through this formation and into the upper mixed hill forest.

Mixed hill dipterocarp forest

In this main canopy at the lower altitudes up to 500 m, there are still some wild mangoes, such as *Mangifera applanata, M. caesia, M. decandra, M. griffithii, M. pajang*, and *M. torquenda* (Anacardiaceae), with *Canarium megalanthum*, and *Dacryodes rostrata* (Burseraceae). The Fagaceae (oaks and chestnuts) become more common above 300 m, including the lowland *Castanopsis megacarpa*.

Parkia speciosa (Fabaceae) appears to be more common in the hill forest than lowland forest and *Pometia pinnata* (Sapindaceae) more common along the rivers.

Understorey trees below 35 m tall with edible fruits are still plentiful here, such as species of *Dimocarpus, Lepisanthes* and *Nephelium* (Sapindaceae), *Baccaurea* spp. (Phyllanthaceae) and *Garcinia* species (Clusiaceae). However, *Artocarpus* (Moraceae) species that have large leaves are much less common, such as *Artocarpus brevipedunculatus, A. lanceifolius, A. rigidus* and *A. tamaran,* while *Ficus* is represented by the edible earth figs *Ficus uncinata* and *F. nota*; however, many other species of *Ficus* are edible to birds and mammals.

In the Malvaceae, the only common hill durian species are *Durio dulcis, D. crassipes* and *D. kinabaluensis* in Sabah; however, in the villages cultivated lowland species, such as *D. zibethinus, D. oxleyanus* and *D. graveolens*, are common together with several other lowland fruit trees not normally found in the hill forest above 300 m.

Understorey trees with edible fruits or that become more common in the hill forest, that are consumed by hunters and forest gatherers, are *Saurauia* spp. (Actinidiaceae), *Antidesma* spp. (Phyllanthaceae), *Sarcotheca diversifolia* (Oxalidaceae), *Litsea garciae* (Lauraceae), *Alangium javanicum* (Cornaceae), *Pangium edule* (Achariaceae), *Sandoricum* and *Walsura* spp. (Meliaceae), *Xanthophyllum* spp. (Polygalaceae), *Heliciopsis artocarpoides* (Proteaceae), *Canarium odontophyllum* (Burseraceae), *Elateriospermum tapos* (Euphorbiaceae) and *Gnetum gnemon* (Gnetaceae). *Glenniea philippinensis* (Sapindaceae) is one of the very rare hill understorey trees.

Many of the climbers with edible fruits also extend into the mixed hill forest, such as *Uvaria grandiflora* (Annonaceae), *Willughbeia* spp. (Apocynaceae) and the rattans or climbing palms such as *Calamus, Daemonorops* and *Korthalsia* spp. in the Arecaceae.

Below the understorey trees are small treelets, shrubs and herbs, several having edible fruits, and these generally become more diverse in the hill forest. Among the treelets are *Flacourtia rukam* (Salicaceae), several edible *Salacca* palms (Arecaceae), and shrubs and small treelet species of *Melastoma*

(Melastomaceae) seen on landslides, forest-gaps, road sides and streams, together with shrubs of *Rubus* species (Rosaceae). *Rubus moluccanus* is a scrambling climber-bramble over branches amongst the shrubs and treelets.

Among herbs, *Molineria latifolia* (Hypoxidaceae) becomes more common, and the wild banana *Musa lawitiensis* (Musaceae) with edible fruits is utilised by hill tribes. The gingers (Zingiberaceae) also become more common with altitude, and the higher rainfall, and many species with edible fruits are found in the genera *Alpinia, Etlingera* and *Hornstedtia,* and are utilised by the hill tribes.

6. Upper Hill Mixed Forest (800–1200 m)

This forest formation is also very extensive, and forms a large proportion of Borneo's Central Range, which starts with the Crocker Range in the north in Sabah down through Sarawak, and its borders with North, East and Central Kalimantan. Offshoots of mountain ranges are also found on the eastern side of Sabah, as well as East, South and West Kalimantan, some of which are found on limestone, ultramafic, volcanic or granitic rocks. Most of the forest is on steep ridges, but also on plateaus, and is often crossed with small to large valleys.

Many of the edible fruit tree species found in the lower hill forest continue to occur in this formation, but generally at a much lower frequency. These include *Litsea garciae*, for example. Durian species are far fewer too, the principal species adapted to these altitudes being *Durio kinabaluensis.* Different species of mangoes are also fewer, but include *Mangifera decandra*, *M. foetida* and *M. rufocostata.* Some hill tribes still successfully cultivate popular species normally found at lower altitudes.

We continue to find different species of wild mangosteens such as *Garcinia forbesii* and *G. microcarpa* and *tampois* such as *Baccaurea macrocarpa, B. lanceolata, B. odoratissima* and *B. tetrandra.*

Although fig species are common, only *Ficus nota* and *F. uncinata* are commonly consumed by the hill tribes.

Other species that become less common in this formation are *sentul, Sandoricum koetjape,* and *Lepisanthes* spp. in the Sapindaceae. Wild rambutan species are also still found, but are less common, such as *Nephelium maingayi, N. ramboutan-ake, N. papillatum* and *Pometia pinnata* along the streams.

The herb-layer supports many species of gingers (Zingiberaceae) with edible fruits, and one species of banana, *Musa lawitiensis,* is particularly utilised by hill tribes in Sarawak.

A Guide to Wild Fruits of Borneo

7. *Lower Montane Forest*

This forest formation covers over 10% of Borneo, mainly in the central mountain ranges, with a large percentage now within fully protected areas.

The rattan palms (Arecaceae), often with edible fruit, have species in several genera such as *Calamus*.

Among the few species with large leaves and edible fruits that just reach into the zone are *Artocarpus elasticus* and *Heliciopsis artocarpoides*.

The Fagaceae are widespread, with the hill forest species *Castanopsis megacarpa* just reaching into this formation. More common are *C. costata*, *C. foxworthyi* and *C. endertii*.

Several woody climbers in the genus *Gnetum* (Gnetaceae) occur here, some of which are reported to have edible seeds.

Other fruit trees with edible fruits that are more common in hill forest but reach into this zone include *Baccaurea macrocarpa*, *B. lanceolata*, and *B. odoratissima* in the Phyllanthaceae, *Alangium javanicum* in the Cornaceae, *Xanthophyllum stipitatum* in the Polygalaceae, and *Ficus nota* in the Moraceae.

The only durian reaching this zone is *Durio kinabaluensis* (Malvaceae).

In the moist to wet understorey (due to cloud cover and high rainfall), are *Ficus uncinata* (Moraceae) and the mountain banana, *Musa montana*

Lower montane forest

(Musaceae), with edible fruits. Also in the understorey are a few *Xerospermum* species in the Sapindaceae with small edible rambutan-like fruits.

On the more exposed ridge tops, or where landslides occur, or along roads, can be found several species of *Melastoma* (Melastomaceae) and shrubs such as *Rubus fraxinifolius*, *R. lowii* and *R. rosifolius* in the Rosaceae with edible fruits. The herbs include gingers (Zingiberaceae) and *Molineria latifolia* (Hypoxidaceae).

8. *Upper Montane Forest*

The montane forest formation is found on all the high mountain peaks over 1800 m, and is only extensive along the top of the main central mountain range, covering less than 5% of Borneo.

Figs are present but only *Ficus uncinata* as an understorey tree with edible fruits is present at the lower altitudes below 2200 m. Other tree species with edible fruits and nuts apart from chestnuts (*Castanopsis*) are largely unknown.

As in the lower montane forest, shrub species in *Rubus* (Rosaceae), such as *R. fraxinifolius* and *R. lowii*, are to be found in more open areas, as are treelets and shrubs of *Melastoma* species, some of which have edible fruits.

Upper montane forest

9. *Heath Forest — Lowland, Hill & Montane*

In Borneo this formation is called *kerangas,* an Iban term for forest that after clearing will not grow hill rice. This forest is found growing on coarse sandy soils derived from sandstone formations and other siliceous parent rocks.

The coastal heath forests are generally poor in species with edible fruits, with some coastal forest species present such as the shrub *Rhodomyrtus tomentosa* and *Melastoma malabathricum.*

Lowland to hill heath forest is found inland often surrounded by mixed dipterocarp forest. Some of the forest around the edges consists of taller trees including some dipterocarps and some of the lowland forest fruit trees, but in the tree stands of actual heath forest, edible fruit trees are uncommon. However, *Lansium domesticum*, *Xanthophyllum stipitatum* and *Garcinia* species such as *G. parvifolia*, have been recorded.

At higher altitudes above 700 m, *Garcinia bancana*, *G. rheedei* and other *Garcinia* species have been recorded. Of the edible nuts *Castanopsis foxworthyi* has also been found in hill heath forest.

Heath forest

10. *Limestone Forest — Lowland, Hill and Montane*

Limestone outcrops occur all over Borneo, mostly as isolated craggy hills. However, a few ranges have peaks of 1300–1700 m but these are not so common.

Trees with edible fruits and nuts are not as diverse as in mixed lowland and hill dipterocarp forest, but one of the main canopy trees is *Scorodocarpus borneensis* with edible nuts.

Main canopy to understorey fruit trees include *Pometia pinnata* which is common, and also recorded are *tampois* such as *Baccaurea lanceolata*, *langsat, Lansium domesticum, kesusu, Artocarpus limpato* and several mangosteen species such as *Garcinia forbesii*, *G. parvifolia* and *G. nervosa*.

However there is a rich community of forest floor species including gingers (Zingiberaceae) and *Molineria latifolia* with edible fruits.

The only other edible fruits are from the shrubby wild raspberries, *Rubus* species.

Limestone forest.

Limestone forest

11. *Forests on Ultramafic Soils (Lowland to Montane)*

Ultramafic soils are derived from igneous rocks, mainly serpentinite and peridotite, and are high in iron, manganese and heavy metals such as nickel, chromium, and cobalt, with low silica content (less than 45%).

The most important factors of these soils that affect plant growth include high exchangeable magnesium content but low exchangeable calcium. They are also low in available potassium and phosphorus and high in phytoxic minerals such as nickel and cobalt.

Overall it is estimated there are over 3500 plant species in ultramafic vegetation in Borneo. However, this diversity of plants covers very few species with fruits edible for humans. In the Meratus Mountains in South Kalimantan surveys showed there was a low density of mammals in the ultramafic forests compared to adjacent forests, and that this was linked to a low density of species of edible fruit trees.

In the tall lowland dipterocarp forest around Kinabalu, before much of it was destroyed by forest clearing and fires, the only trees with edible fruits were *Xanthophyllum stipitatum*, *Baccaurea lanceolata*, *Garcinia* and *Saurauia* species. On these soils several *Salacca* palm species, possibly with edible fruits, also occur. In the montane forest the shrubs *Rubus lowii* and *Rubus lineatus* are found on these soils with edible fruits.

Ultramafic forest

A Selection of Species

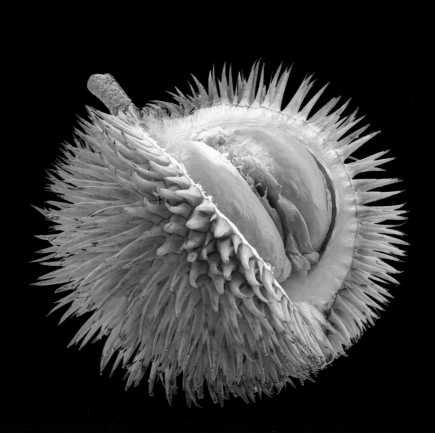

Pangium edule Reinw.

Description: Commonly a dioecious tree to 20 m with small buttresses, but also reaching 45 m with large fluted buttresses, with a bole to 5 m. The leaves are spirally arranged in clusters, with large cordate (heart-shaped) blades. The petioles 10–20(–30) cm, with a proximal pulvinus. The blades mostly glabrous, 20–30 × 15–25 cm. The male inflorescences arise from the leaf axils and have racemes of several greenish, to white or cream flowers which are slightly scented. Female flowers are solitary in the upper leaf axils. The fruits are large, nearly pear-shaped with blunt tips at both ends, with a thick, scurfy, brown epicarp, enclosing over 20 seeds covered in a thick yellow pulp. The fruit stalk is 8–15 cm with 1–3 fruits hanging in a cluster, the fruits are 15–25 × 7–15 cm, each 1.5–2 kg. The seeds are 4 × 3 cm and are flattened, and comprise a cream-coloured, hard testa (endocarp) with distinct veins, enclosing an edible kernel that is rich in fats or oils. They have to be treated to remove poisonous glucosides.

Distribution and Habitat: Throughout Malesia to Micronesia. Often near streams, in primary and secondary lowland and hill dipterocarp forests up to 1000 m.

Vernacular Names: *kepayang* (Malay); *pangi* (Philippines).

Notes: The yellow pulp is sweet and edible, but can only be eaten in small quantities. If the poisonous seeds are boiled, the kernels removed and washed in water several times, they become edible and tasty, and are often cooked with meat or fish. The kernels can be pressed for cooking oil. If the kernels are fermented, they become even tastier. The tree is often cultivated, but is less popular now. The treated or fermented kernels are often sold in local markets.

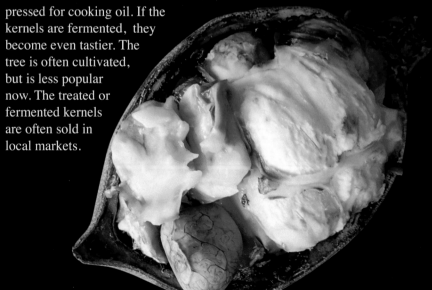

Saurauia glabra Merr.

Description: Understorey small tree to 12 m, bole 2–3 m, no buttresses. Leaves simple, spirally arranged, no stipules, petioles glabrous, variable in length on the same twig, 2–4–8 cm long, 5 mm thick with ridges. Blades glabrous, lanceolate-elliptic to oblanceolate, 17–30(–100) × 6–15–30–50 cm, apex acuminate, base cuneate to obtuse, margin toothed. Upper surface with midvein and laterals distinct and slightly raised, prominent on lower surface, and 10–14(–20) pairs of lateral veins. Inflorescences ramiflorous, with clusters of up to 30 racemes bearing white flowers on twigs below the leaves and along the branches, with 1–3 fruits developing on peduncles 1–1.3 cm and pedicels 2.3–2.5 cm. The fruit a globose berry 1.5 × 1.5 cm, with overlapping, free, persistent calyx lobes at the base, and persistent style, ripening green to yellowish green, carpels sometimes splitting. The epicarp 1 mm thick, covering a mass of tiny seeds in a sweet slimy jelly.

Distribution and Habitat: Endemic to Borneo. In hill to lower montane forest, on steep slopes as well as along river banks, 500–1200 m. Also on ultramafic and limestone soils.

Vernacular Names: *mata ikan* (Malay); *longugan* (Sabah).

Notes: This is one of many species of *Saurauia* found in Borneo that have edible fruits. Several species of this genus with edible fruits are also recorded for Peninsular Malaysia, Java, Sumatra and the Philippines. The fruits are generally more of a famine food, or are eaten by hunter-gatherers, as they are not particularly tasty and are rather similar to the Chinese gooseberry or Kiwi fruit. The fresh fruits are eaten by squeezing out the pulp and seeds as a juice, and are popular with village children. The fruits are also a favourite of palm civets and slow lorises.

Bouea oppositifolia (Roxb.) Meisn.

Description: Small to medium deciduous tree, 10–20 m, bole short 1–2 m, low branching with a dense round canopy and arching branches. Leaves simple, opposite, glabrous and leathery, petioles 1–1.7 cm, grooved above, with small stipules, blades elliptic to oblong, 3–10(–15) × 1.5–3–5 cm, base obtuse, apex acute, with prominent midvein on both surfaces with 8–17 pairs of lateral veins faintly visible. Inflorescence a short pendulous panicle from branches, or axils of leaves 2–6 cm long, with small white to pale yellow flowers. Fruit a drupe, globose to ovoid, 1.5–1.8(–2.5) × 1–1.5(–2.5) cm. Epicarp thin, smooth, greenish-yellow to pale yellow or orange to red when ripe. Pulp or mesocarp whitish to pale yellow, edible, sour to sweet with fibres. Seed a stone 1–1.5 cm with fibrous, leathery endocarp and violet purple cotyledons.

Distribution and Habitat: Indochina, Myanmar, Peninsular Malaysia, Peninsular Thailand, Sumatra, Sulawesi and Borneo. Found in lowland mixed dipterocarp forest, coastal forest, and peatswamp forests to 700 m.

Vernacular Names: *kundangan, kundang* or *remenia* (Malay); plum mango (English).

Notes: Today, many areas of peatswamp forests where this species used to be found have been destroyed by fires, and the species now appears to be uncommon in most parts of Borneo. *Bouea macrophylla* Griff., which probably still occurs in the wild in Kalimantan but is widely cultivated (also commercially), is very similar, with larger leaves to 30 × 11 cm and up to 25 pairs of lateral veins. There appear to be several other unidentified species of *Bouea* in Borneo that are similar to *B. oppositifolia*.

Dracontomelon dao (Blanco) Merr. & Rolfe

Description: Tree 25–40 m. Bole c. 5 m with large buttresses. Leaves compound, pinnate, clustered toward the ends of the twigs. Petiole and rachis to 75 cm long with up to 20 pairs of alternate leaflets in a lateral plane, petiolules 3 mm, leaflet blades ovate elliptic to oblong or obovate, 5–30 × 3–10 cm, glabrous, with rounded base and acute apex with 6–20 pairs of lateral veins. Inflorescences terminal, panicle 25–50 cm with small urn-shaped, white flowers. Fruits globose with 5 locules, to 2.2–3 cm diameter, ripening to brownish-purple, with thin, leathery epicarp, a thick, fibrous, white, juicy, edible mesocarp which is sweet but with little flavour. The light brown seed is 1.1 cm × 6–7 mm.

Distribution and Habitat: Eastern India, Myanmar, Thailand, Cambodia, China, Malesia to Solomon Islands. In lowland mixed dipterocarp forest, common along streams and rivers up to 200 m.
Vernacular Names: *sengkuang* (Malay); *seronsob* (general).
Notes: Rarely cultivated and seldom sold in local markets. Generally eaten by hunter-gatherers, or harvested from trees along the rivers in nearby villages. The other Bornean species, *D. costatum* Blume, has very poor quality edible fruits.

Mangifera caesia Jack

Description: Deciduous tree to 40 m, bole to 15 m, without buttresses, with a large crown. Leaves simple, seasonally falling off (deciduous period), but for a short period only, and new flushes are produced in spirally arranged whorls. Petioles 1–3 cm long, flattened above, with leaf margins or wings along sides, base thickened (proximal pulvinus), no stipules. Blade broadly lanceolate to elliptic to obovate, 6–20(–40) × 3–6(–10) cm, base alternate, apex acute to obtuse, midvein prominent on both surfaces with 10–33 pairs of lateral veins, thick and leathery to stiff. Inflorescences pseudo-terminal panicles to 30 cm long, branching, the glabrous, reddish peduncles and branches with many flowers, the flowers densely arranged, pale lilac to mauve and fragrant. Fruit ellipsoid drupe, 1.2–1.5 cm long × 6–10 cm wide. Epicarp thin with several varieties, some glossy, greenish-yellow to green, glabrous, others with yellowish-brown scurfy surface, the former has white pulp or mesocarp that is sweet, soft, with yellow fibres, juicy with a strong smell. The brownish form usually has a sour, fibrous white pulp. Seed (stone) ellipsoid, 6.5–7 × 3.5–4 cm, with hard, fibrous endocarp.

Distribution and Habitat: Peninsular Malaysia, Sumatra and Borneo. In lowland mixed dipterocarp forest often on alluvial soil, but also in hill forest up to 400 m. Widely cultivated for its fruits.

Vernacular Name: *beluno* (Malay).

Notes: Very distinct tree with lilac-coloured flowers, and fruits heavily in most years. The sour forms are usually eaten as a sambal.

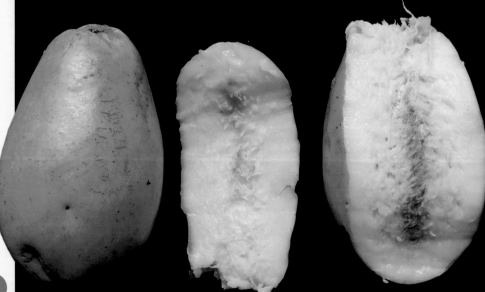

Mangifera casturi Kosterm.

Description: Tree to 25 m, bole 15 m with small buttresses and spreading globose crown (cauliflower shape) like *M. laurina* Blume. Leaves simple, spirally arranged, glabrous, petioles 2–4(–8) cm with proximal pulvinus or thickening basally, no stipules. Blade oblong to elliptic, base acute, apex shortly acuminate, 15–19(–28) × 3–5(–7) cm, midvein prominent on both surfaces with 16–25 pairs of lateral veins. Inflorescences pseudo-terminal panicles covering the whole tree as in *M. laurina*, to 30 cm long with wide basal branches, rachis yellowish green with very short hairs (puberulous) with sub-glomerate flowers. Flowers fragrant, pale green and white, with reflexed petals, turning pale pink. Fruit a drupe—there are several varieties with different shapes. Generally ovoid with rose red to purple epicarp (kasturi), with some turning black (cuban variety, usually 5–6 × 3.5–4.5 cm), others with ellipsoid fruits and remaining green (pelipisan variety, usually 5–6 × 2.5–3 cm). Pulp or mesocarp dark orange, sweet and juicy, fibrous. Seed (stone) 4.5–5(–6) cm × 2.5–3 × 1.5–3 cm, with hard endocarp with fibres and longitudinal furrows or grooves.

Distribution and Habitat: Endemic to Borneo (Kalimantan only). Now only known in cultivation, probably because lowland forests where it originally occurred have all been cleared.

Vernacular Names: *mangga kasturi* (Malay); *cuban* or *palipisan* (Kalimantan).

Notes: This is a popular fruit in Kalimantan. Like *M. laurina*, the tree produces a spectacular mass of flowers, and the leaves and flowers appear to be resistant to anthracnose disease.

Mangifera decandra Ding Hou

Description: Tree to 50 m, deciduous. Bole to 20 m with no buttresses. Leaves simple, glabrous, spirally arranged and crowded near the ends of the twigs. Petioles 2–6 cm long, often thickened over most of its length, no stipules. Blades elliptic-oblong to obovate-oblong, 17–27(–40) × 7–12(–15) cm, apex mucronate, base cuneate, margin entire, veins with midvein and lateral veins raised on both surfaces, with 17–27 pairs of lateral veins (35–40 pairs in saplings). Inflorescences pseudo-terminal, 15–65 cm long with basal branches to 25 cm, densely hairy (puberulous). Flowers reddish to pink. Fruit a broadly ellipsoid drupe, 12–16 × 8–10.5 cm, with a rough (rugose), yellowish to brown epicarp of 1 mm thick. Mesocarp or pulp whitish, with very woolly fibres, (6 cm long), sour and acidic. Seed (stone) 9–11 × 4.5–5.5 cm.

Distribution and Habitat: Sumatra and Borneo. It is widespread but scattered in lowland mixed dipterocarp forest, but is also found in hill forest up to 900 m and sometimes in swampy forest. Seldom cultivated—fruits are collected from the forest.
Vernacular Names: *binjai hutan* (Malay); *belunu hutan* (Sabah).
Notes: The species in this subgenus are separated into trees that are deciduous (dropping their leaves seasonally), including *M. pajang* Kosterm., *M. caesia* Jack and *M. decandra*, and those that are not deciduous, such as *M. foetida* Lour. and *M. macrocarpa* Blume. The very fibrous, sour fruit makes it a neglected fruit.

Mangifera foetida Lour.

Description: Species in this section of the subgenus *Limus* are not deciduous. Tree 20 m to 30 m, bole to 7 m, without buttresses, with a rounded, dense crown. Leaves simple, spirally arranged and scattered along twigs, to crowded at ends of twigs. Petioles 2–5(–10) cm, flattened above, with proximal pulvinus, and no stipules. Blades elliptic to oblong to oblanceolate, base acute to obtuse, apex acute to obtuse, glabrous, 12–30 × 6–10(–15) cm, leathery, stiff, midvein prominent with 15–21 pairs of lateral veins. Inflorescence a pseudo-terminal, pyramidal panicle, usually glabrous to 30 cm long with red peduncle and branches, and dense glomerules of fragrant, red flowers. Fruit a subglobose drupe, 10–14 × 10 cm, epicarp green to yellowish green or brownish with scattered dark brown spots, 5 mm thick with irritant sap, mesocarp or pulp very fibrous, yellow, sweet, with a pleasant flavour, but turpentine smell.

Distribution and Habitat: Peninsular Malaya, Sumatra, West Java, Moluccas and Borneo. In lowland mixed dipterocarp forest, and hill forest to 400 m, also found in swamp areas. Widely cultivated.
Vernacular Names: *embangor* or *macang* (Malay); *bacang* & *pauh* (general); horse mango (English).
Notes: When in bloom with its bright red panicles of flowers, this species is a magnificent ornamental tree, although it has not been utilised for this purpose despite being widely cultivated in many kampongs. The kernel (endosperm) in the stone of this species is also grated and mixed with salt, sugar and fermented fish in sambals.

Mangifera griffithii Hook. f.

Description: Tree up to 30–40 m tall, bole to 20 m, no buttresses. Leaves simple, glabrous, leathery, stiff, spirally arranged, new flush leaves pale purple. Petiole 1–2 cm, with short proximal pulvinus and no stipules. Blade elliptic to obovate 5–9(–18) × 3–4(–7) cm, base cuneate, apex acute or obtuse, midvein prominent on both surfaces, with 9–12 pairs of lateral veins. Inflorescence an axillary or terminal panicle, 10–25 cm, pubescent, with few short branches with small whitish flowers, densely glomerate. Fruit an ellipsoid to oblong drupe, 2.5–3.5 × 1.5–2.5 cm, yellowish or pink to rose-red, sometimes turning purplish black, the smooth, thin epicarp covering a sweet-sour, orange-yellow pulp which is juicy and edible with thin fibres. Seed with leathery fibrous endocarp, 3–3.5 × 2–2.5 cm.

Distribution and Habitat: Peninsular Malaysia, Sumatra, Borneo. Found in lowland mixed dipterocarp forest often in swamp areas up to 400 m.

Notes: It is often cultivated, but does not produce fruit regularly, and is now becoming rarer.

Mangifera laurina Blume

Description: Tree to 36 m, bole 3–5 m, often with short buttresses. Leaves simple, petiole 2–5–8 cm with proximal pulvinus and no stipules. Blade elliptic-lanceolate to oblong to lanceolate, 6–30 × 3–7 cm, base acute, apex acuminate, margins slightly undulate, midvein prominent on both surfaces, with 15–30 pairs of lateral veins. Inflorescences pseudo-terminal panicles, mostly glabrous, with greenish white peduncle and branches to 40 cm long, bearing white to cream to pale yellow fragrant flowers, flowers not clustered or glomerate (as in *M. indica* L., which also has indumentum on the panicle). Fruit a drupe 6–10 × 4–6 cm with typical mango shape, epicarp thin, greenish yellow, smooth, mesocarp or pulp yellow, watery when fully ripe, sweet, with thin fibres. Seed (stone) flattened, with fibrous, furrowed (grooved) endocarp, 4.5–5.5 × 2–3 cm.

Distribution and Habitat: Malesia region. In all states of Borneo. In lowlands up to 150 m.

Vernacular Names: *mangga air* (Sabah); *mangga parih* (Java).

Notes: When in flower the whole "cauliflower-like" canopy is covered in cream to whitish flowers, and is a spectacular sight. This species is distinct from *M. indica*, which has inflorescences with glomerate flowers. It has been noted that *M. laurina* trees all flower at the same time over wide areas in Sabah and at the same time, as the hybrid (previously known as *M. odorata* or kwini), when *M. indica* cultivars are not in flower. Unlike *M. indica*, it is not susceptible to anthracnose.

Mangifera pajang Kosterm.

Description: Deciduous tree to 33 m tall, bole to 7 m, without buttresses and with an open crown. Leaves simple, produces a seasonal flush of new pink leaves, spirally arranged in whorls at the ends of the twigs. Petioles 3.5–9 cm long, upper surface flattened, with swollen proximal pulvinus, no stipules. Blades elliptic to oblong to obovate, thick, stiff, 15–28(–45) × 7–10(–15) cm; base cuneate, apex obtuse, with prominent midvein and laterals, and 14–30 pairs of lateral veins. The large leaves with distinct veins make the tree easy to recognise. Inflorescences panicles, often terminal or from axils of upper leaves, erect, glabrous, to 30 cm, with pink to red and white flowers that are fragrant, making it a very attractive tree for ornamental use. Fruit a large drupe, globose to globose-ellipsoid, with a thick, rugose, brown epicarp to 1 cm thick, 10–12 × 8.5–10 cm. Mesocarp fibrous, juicy, sweet. There are reportedly four varieties with distinct flavours. Of the two more common varieties, one has smaller, sweeter and juicier fruits, while the other has larger, less juicy, less sweet fruits with pulp that is paler yellow in colour. Seed (stone) 9–12 × 6–7 cm, endocarp woody, 5 mm thick.

Distribution and Habitat: Endemic to Borneo, rare in lowland to hill mixed dipterocarp forest, to 500 m, not found in swampy areas. Widely cultivated in villages all over Borneo up to 1000 m.
Vernacular Names: *bambangan* (Sabah); *embang* (Sarawak); *bembangan* (Brunei).
Notes: The species produces one of the best tasting mango juices. In Sabah, the kernel of the seeds is grated and mixed with minced fish pickled in lime juice, and mixed with salt, chillies, ginger or onions to make a sambal called '*jerok bambangan*' or '*hinava*'. Recently, bottled jams and juices are being produced locally. Hybrids with *M. foetida* Lour. have been recorded.

Mangifera pentandra Hook. f.

Description: Tree to 28 m, bole to 5 m, mostly with no buttresses or with very short, thick ones. Leaves simple, spirally arranged, often in whorls at the ends of the twigs, young leaves purple turning yellow, and then green, petiole glabrous, 3–6 cm, flattish above, with proximal pulvinus and no stipules. Blade oblong to elliptic, 11–35 × 4–10 cm, midveins raised on both surfaces, 12–23 pairs of lateral veins, base obtuse, apex acuminate. Inflorescences pseudo-terminal, pyramidal panicles to 15–35 cm with dense hairs on the peduncles and branches, becoming glabrous, flowers with five tepals, pale yellow to creamy to white. Fruit an oblong drupe, 6–10 × 4.5–6 cm, green to yellow when ripe, thin epicarp, pulp around seed pale orange, juicy, sweet, with some fibres. Seed oblong 4–5 × 3–3.5 cm, flattened, with deep furrows and short fibres.

Distribution and Habitat: Peninsular Malaysia and Borneo (Sabah only). There are some old trees in the coastal forest on the West Coast.
Vernacular Names: *mangga dodol* (Malay); plum mango (English)*; mangga telur* (Sabah).
Notes: In Sabah, the ripe fruits are yellow,
thin-skinned, with a juicy, often sweet,
orange pulp that is often sucked out.
It only flowers and fruits every few years.

Mangifera quadrifida Jack

Description: Tree 30–40 m, bole 20 m, some with small buttresses, with a very dense, dark green crown which is glabrous in all parts. Leaves spirally arranged, shining dark green, varying a lot in size, petioles 1.5–5 cm (when petioles are shorter, the proximal pulvinus covers their whole length), with no stipules. Blade 8–10(–20) × 2–4(–9) cm, elliptic to oblong to spathulate, base cuneate, apex acute or obtuse, midvein prominent on both surfaces with 9–15 pairs of lateral veins. Inflorescences pseudo-terminal and axillary short, pyramidal panicles to 12 cm, with dense, glabrous, white flowers. Fruits globose to ellipsoid, 5–6(–8) × 5–6 cm, green epicarp ripening to black, thin, to 2 mm. Mesocarp or pulp yellow to orange, with some fibres, juicy, sweet, edible with pleasant odour. Seed (stone) with leathery, fibrous, hard endocarp 4–5 × 2.5–3.5 cm. Usually a heavy bearer when it fruits.

Distribution and Habitat: Peninsular Malaysia, Sumatra, Borneo (in all states), Sulawesi to Sunda Islands and Moluccas. In lowland and hill mixed dipterocarp forest, more common on alluvial flood plains and riverine forest, to 600 m.

Vernacular Names: *asam kumbang* (Malay); *rawa*, *rawa-rawa* (Borneo); *rancha-rancha* (Sabah).

Notes: This small purple, plum-sized mango, is now becoming rarer in Sabah and Sarawak. It probably has an infrequent fruiting season and is being replaced by *M. indica* L. cultivars.

Mangifera torquenda Kosterm.

Description: Tree to 40 m, bole to 10 m, but with low branches in more open areas. Buttresses not seen, crown globose and dark green. Leaves simple, glabrous, spirally arranged and scattered along twigs, forming whorls near apices of twigs. Petioles long, slender, 5–15 cm, with distinct proximal pulvinus of 10–15 mm with no stipules. Blade usually elliptic to oblong, 17–21 × 6–9 cm, base cuneate to rounded, apex acute to acuminate, glossy, dark green on upper surface, midvein prominent on both surfaces with 16–20 pairs of lateral veins. Inflorescence pseudo-terminal panicles to 25 cm with slender branches, pubescent at base, with white to pale yellow fragrant flowers. Fruit globose, 7.5–10 × 6.5–8.5 cm with small beak, epicarp thin, to 2 mm, greenish yellow when ripe, with spots and brown patches. Pulp or mesocarp pale yellow, sweet to acidic, with short fibres, very tasty, with slight turpentine fragrance. Seed (stone) 6–7(–8.5) × 4–5 cm, with white smooth endocarp with short fibres and with grooves.

Distribution and Habitat: Peninsular Malaysia, Sumatra and Borneo. In lowland to hill mixed dipterocarp forest to 800 m. Uncommon in Sabah and Sarawak. Cultivated in East Kalimantan.

Vernacular Names: *lamantan* (Malay); *buniton* (Sabah); *kemantan* (Iban).

Notes: The species gets its name from how the fruits are opened by cutting around the middle and twisting them. The fruits are mainly collected from forest trees, and are not common except in East Kalimantan where the trees are cultivated around villages. Because it is sour, the pulp is often used in sambal or cooked with fish. The juice is used in cordials.

Description: A medium-sized tree to 36 m, bole c. 5 m with spreading buttresses. Leaves compound pinnate, petiole and rachis 10–30 cm (petiole 10 cm), rachis with 7–9 rows of opposite leaflets with a terminal leaflet, petiolules 1–5 mm, blades elliptic-oblong or ovate, 5–13 × 2–6 cm, base obtuse to rounded, apex acute, with 6–10 pairs of lateral veins. Inflorescences to 30 cm long, terminal, pyramidal panicles of small white flowers. Fruits sharply pointed, ovoid to ovoid oblong, greenish with brown spots, 2.5–5 × 1.8–2.75 cm, with thin leathery exocarp, very fibrous mesocarp, and ovoid-oblong, compressed seed, hard endocarp 1 mm thick, with white edible kernel of 2.5 cm long × 1.3 cm wide, and 4 mm thick.

Distribution and Habitat: Sumatra, Peninsular Malaysia, Borneo, New Guinea to Solomon Islands. Lowland mixed dipterocarp forest to 300 m, often along rivers, along which the floating seeds are distributed.
Vernacular Names: *pelajau* (Malay); *empelanjau* (Iban).
Notes: The species flowers twice a year, losing the leaves (deciduous) before flowering with new leaves. The kernels have a delicious nutty flavour, and are often fried or boiled with vegetables.

Stelechocarpus burahol (Blume) Hook. f. & Thomson

Description: Understorey monoecious tree to 25 m tall, bole 3–4 m, covered in tubercles. Leaves simple, alternate in a lateral plane, stipules absent, petioles 0.5–1.5 cm long, glabrous. Blade elliptic to oblong, sometimes lanceolate, 8–27 × 2–3–9 cm, apex acute to acuminate, base cuneate to obtuse, margin entire. Upper surface glabrous, midvein prominent, lower surface glabrous to sparsely pubescent with brown dots, veins prominent, with 8–10 pairs of lateral veins. Both male and female inflorescences on the same tree: male inflorescences ramiflorous from woody tubercles on branches or upper bole, with white flowers of 1 cm diameter on c. 1.8 cm long pedicels in a cluster, female inflorescences cauliflorous on tubercles on the bole, with a cluster of 8–15 white flowers to 3 cm diameter, with pedicels 2–10 cm long, producing a cluster of 1–13 fruits. Fruits obovoid to globose, berry-like carpels, 3–5(–6) cm diameter, on pedicels to 8 cm long, epicarp brown, scurfy when ripe, with 2–3 seeds, 2–4 cm long in each section with a whitish, sweet, juicy mesocarp or pulp around the seeds.

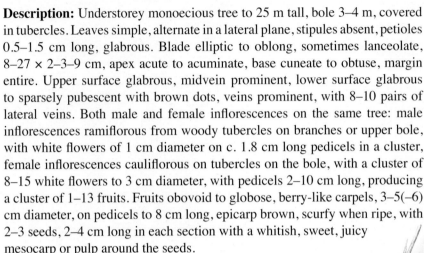

Distribution and Habitat: Southern Peninsular Malaysia, Sumatra, Java, Bali and Borneo (Sarawak & Kalimantan only). Commonly cultivated in Java. In lowland to hill mixed dipterocarp forest to 600 m.

Vernacular Names:
kepel (Malay);
kepel apple (English).

Notes: This species is sometimes placed in the genus *Sageraea*, which has 9 species and is closely related to *Stelechocarpus*. Traditionally, the fruits were only allowed to be eaten in the courts of the sultans in Java, Borneo and Johore, as it made sweat and urine smell like violets! Now it is commonly sold in markets in Java.

Uvaria grandiflora Roxb. ex Hornem.

Description: Woody climber to 20 m, lower stem or bole to 15 m. Leaves simple, alternate and laterally arranged on twigs, petiole 7–10 mm, grooved, hairy. Blade elliptic to oblong to oblanceolate, 12–20(–30) × 5–7(–9) cm, apex acuminate, base subcordate to rounded, margin entire. Upper surface glabrous, midvein sunken, laterals flat, lower surface pubescent, veins prominent, with 10–17 pairs of lateral veins. Inflorescence a cyme, terminal and opposite the apical leaf of the twig, with a solitary or 2–3 flowers. Flowers bisexual, with large red petals to 4.5–6 cm diameter. Fruits 3–10 or more developing on a pendulous peduncle to 3.5 cm long, fruits a cylindrical berry-like carpel (monocarp) 4–8 cm long, with constrictions between segments. Epicarp 1 mm thick, with a rugose surface ripening yellow to orange, covering 2 rows of seeds in white, edible, aromatic pulp.

Distribution and Habitat: India, Sri Lanka, southern China, Myanmar, Thailand, Indochina, Peninsular Malaysia, Sumatra, Java, Philippines and Borneo. In lowland to hill mixed dipterocarp forest.

Vernacular Names: *pisang akar* (Malay); *pisang-pisang* (Sabah); *kalak* (Indon).

Notes: The pulp and seeds are eaten fresh or sometimes made into a preserve. This plant is rarely cultivated, but when it is, it is grown mainly as an ornamental climber for its large red flowers.

Willughbeia angustifolia (Miq.) Markgr.

Description: A woody, monoecious climber, with pendulous branches in the canopy of forest trees, to 60 m tall, with white latex. The twigs produce tendrils from modified inflorescences. The leaves are glabrous, simple and opposite, with petioles 0.4–1.7 cm long and no stipules. The blade is ovate to elliptic and variable in size from 2.6–20.5 × 0.9–7 cm, apex obtuse to acuminate, base rounded to cuneate, margin entire, surfaces glabrous with veins indistinct, flat above, midvein prominent below with 9–24 pairs of indistinct lateral veins. Inflorescences up to 3 in axils of leaves, flowers in short cymes to 1.7 cm long with 5–9 flowers, each with five small sepals, and petals forming a distinct, small, inflated corolla tube with white lobes (compared to other species with long corolla tubes). Fruit a fleshy berry, globose to ovoid, 3–14 cm diameter, epicarp to 5 mm thick with white latex contains several seeds that are flattened ovoid, to 1.2–2.4 × 0.6–1.4 cm and covered in an edible, orange sarcotesta that is sweet to sub-acidic with a flavour of raspberries and strawberries. The fruits are considered the best of the species, and often appear in local markets or weekly "tamus".

Distribution and Habitat: southern Thailand, Nicobar Islands, Peninsular Malaysia, Singapore, Sumatra, Moluccas and Borneo. Found in lowland and hill mixed dipterocarp forest, usually in valleys and lower slopes with good organic matter, up to 500 m altitude.

Vernacular Names: *gerit-gerit, gitaan* (Malay); *serapit* (Sabah, Brunei) *akar kubal madu* (Iban).

Notes: This species is considered the sweetest and most delicious in the genus. Several species including this were previously harvested or tapped for latex (Borneo Rubber) before the rubber tree *Hevea brasiliensis* was introduced in 1908.

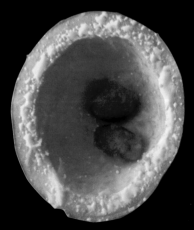 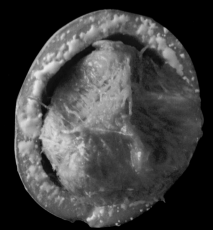

Willughbeia sarawacensis (Pierre) K. Schum.

Description: A woody monoecious climber, covering trees to 35 m, with some pendulous branches near to the ground, and producing a white latex. Leaves, simple, opposite, petioles 1.1–1.8 cm without stipules. Blades oblong to obovate, 6–17 × 3.7–6.6 cm, apex acuminate, base cuneate to obtuse, upper surface glabrous with raised midvein and distinct laterals, lower surface with prominent midvein, sometimes with hairs, lateral veins distinct, 11–19 pairs. Inflorescence from axils of leaves, a short cyme to 2.5 cm with several white flowers with long corolla tube and lobes. Fruit a fleshy berry, only one or two per leaf axil, spherical to ovoid, 8–18 × 6–12 cm, weighing up to 2 kg. Epicarp ripening from green to brown, together with the whitish mesocarp to 5 mm thick, forming a shell or rind. Fruit with 10 or more seeds covered in a thick, white, soft, juicy sarcotesta, sweet with acidic aftertaste and highly sought after. Sadly, rarely seen in markets, and cultivation not known of.

Distribution and Habitat: Philippines (Palawan), Borneo (Brunei, Sabah & Sarawak). In lowland and hill mixed dipterocarp forest to 300 m. It is uncommon to rare in Sabah and Brunei.

Vernacular Names:
kubal tabau (Iban);
pitabu (Brunei).

Notes: This differs from the other edible species which have an orange epicarp, and orange pulp around the seeds.

Daemonorops periacantha Miq.

Description: A climbing, dioecious, rattan palm, branching at the base to form a cluster of stems, climbing to 10 m. The pinnate leaves (fronds) have spiny leaf sheaths covering the stem so that it is 3–8 cm diameter, but when the old leaves fall off, the glabrous stem is 1.5–3 cm diameter with internodes to 35 cm. The leaf sheath covering the stem is green and covered in dense yellow spines which point in all directions and range from short to long, up to 6–8 cm. The base of the petiole where it joins the leaf sheath forms a spiny knee, the green petiole to 50 cm, with 2 lateral yellow lines covered in fans of scattered spines. The rachis to 3 m long has up to 45 lanceolate leaflets, each to 40 × 3 cm, irregularly arranged in groups of 2–7 leaflets on each side. The end of the rachis forms a leafless cirrus (extension of the rachis) to 1.5 m, covered in reflexed spines (acting like grappling hooks) that attach it to surrounding plants. Male and female inflorescences borne on separate plants, are similar, with a panicle up to 1 m long and a peduncle to 50 cm, each young inflorescence subtended and covered by a brown bract with bristles that fall off at flowering. The inflorescences have up to 10 branches (rachillae) either with male flowers, each with a small cup-shaped calyx and 3 small petals, or larger female flowers in pairs. The infructescence has 2 to 6 fruits per branch, each fruit globose to slightly ovoid, to 2.2 cm diameter with a small apical stigma, the epicarp covered in 15 vertical rows of straw to pale brown scales. The drupe contains a single round seed to 1.5 cm diameter, covered in a translucent, sweet-sour, edible sarcotesta.

Distribution and Habitat: Peninsular Malaysia, Sumatra and Borneo. In lowland and hill dipterocarp forest, usually in valleys or lower hill slopes up to 800 m altitude.

Vernacular Names: *rotan jagung, rotan* (Malay); *wi empunok* (Iban); rattan (English).

Notes: Many species of rattan palms have edible fruits which are often also picked when the useful canes are harvested, and sold in markets. Most of the edible species are in the genera *Calamus*, *Daemonorops* and *Korthalsia*.

Eleiodoxa conferta (Griff.) Burret

Description: A trunkless, dioecious, rosette palm, with an underground rhizome (stem) with axillary shoots, and small erect breathing roots, producing a cluster of erect to slanting pinnate leaves (fronds) 4–8 m tall, with petioles to 2–3 m, with whorls of downward pointing, spirally-arranged spines, 3–5(–7) cm long. Rachis of frond with c. 20–25 subopposite leaflets, in 2 rows in a lateral plane, evenly spaced along the rachis, with fans of 3 whitish, reflexed spines, 2–3 cm long, below each leaflet. Leaflets sessile, linear, lanceolate, glabrous, to 75 cm long, 1.5 cm wide at base, 2–5 cm at widest section, tapering to a long-pointed apex with 3 main prominent parallel veins, margins with short spines. Inflorescence terminal from the leaf base, branching panicle initially covered by outer spathes (bracts). The inflorescences are dimorphic, the female and male flowers borne on separate spikes: the male inflorescences up to 60 cm taller than the females ones, with branches to 15 cm and flowers crowded in a dense spiral along the branch. Infructescence forming a dense head of many fruits that are obovoid but flattish on top, 2–3 cm diameter, with a thin epicarp covered in yellow or golden brown, non-thorny scales. The drupe usually contains a single broad seed, covered in a thick, edible, white sarcotesta, which is juicy but sour.

Distribution and Habitat: South Thailand, Peninsular Malaysia, Sumatra and Borneo. In fresh water and peatswamp forest, often in a very muddy wet habitat.

Vernacular Names: *kelubi*, *asam paya* (Malay); *buah maram* (Iban).

Notes: This species was previously included in the genus *Salacca*. *Eleiodoxa* is a monotypic genus with only one species. After flowering and fruiting, the individual rosette dies off. Generally, the fruits are used as a substitute for tamarind or *kandis* (*Garcinia*) species. The sour pulp is used in cooking fish, curries or in sambals. The fruit are also pickled and used like sour plums in drinks. The fruits are sold in local markets all year round. This species is rarely cultivated.

Nypa fruticans Wurmb

Description: A trunkless, monoecious, rosette palm, with a horizontal underground, stout, slightly flattened, branching rhizome, buoyant with sponge tissue, to 60 cm diameter, growing in the liquid mud of tidal swamps and estuarine river banks. The rhizome has a terminal rosette of huge erect pinnate leaves (fronds) 6–9 m tall, petioles to 1 m, flat on upper surface with broad, buoyant base, clasping the rhizome. The 5–8 m long, round rachis has 2 rows of up to 60 leaflets per row, the leaflets laterally arranged, glabrous, upward pointing, lanceolate, 60–130 × 4–6 cm. Inflorescence arising from the rhizome between the fronds, near to the outer part of the rosette, an erect panicle, with a stout peduncle to 90 cm, and a long, basal spathe (bract). The panicle has a few erect main branches with sheathing spathes—the lower ones have cream male flowers, while the apical, terminal spike has female yellow flowers, and forms an infructescence in the form of a head to 60 cm diameter, of chestnut brown, closely packed fruits. Fruits ovoid, 9–12 × 3–4 cm sections, with angular ridges coming to a pointed apex with a persistent, woody stigma. The base of ripe fruits cream, the rest shiny brown. The pericarp (epicarp and mesocarp) forming a thick fibrous layer around a large woody seed, 4–5 × 3–4 cm, with a thin hard endocarp 4 mm thick, and white kernel.

Distribution and Habitat: From Sri Lanka, all through Southeast Asia to northeastern Australia and Solomon Islands. It forms massive colonies in tidal estuarine zones, along the coasts to the upper tidal reaches of rivers, and tolerates brackish to salt water.

Vernacular Names: *nipah* (Malay); *apung* (Iban); mangrove palm, nipa palm (English); attap palm (general).

Notes: *Nypa* is a monotypic genus (with only one species) which has a very ancient origin, with fossil records from many places in the rest of the world dating to the Paleocene and Miocene periods. Today, it is a poorly utilised plant species, although it was widely used in the past, especially for *atap* roofing, and sugar and alcohol production. Only the immature fruits are eaten—when the kernel is still a translucent jelly, it is boiled in syrup and eaten as a sweetmeat.

Salacca affinis Griff.

Description: A forest undergrowth rosette palm, sometimes growing in scattered clumps, the stem short, to c. 0.5 m and mostly obscured by leaf bases. The leaves spirally arranged in the form of erect pinnate fronds to 3 m, the petiole with fans of long spines, the rachis with 2 rows of leaflets in the same plane towards the apex. The linear leaflets are spread in groups of 4–7 along the rachis, separated by irregular gaps, with the leaflets to 40 × 6 cm, with longitudinal veins, and acuminate apex. The palms are dioecious, the inflorescences are separated into those with male or female flowers, and arise from the leaf axils as an erect, branching panicle, on a stout peduncle, with the small erect, spike-like branches partly hidden by subtending spathes consisting of several bracts to 20 cm. Female inflorescences have fewer branchlets than the males, and are 5–7 cm long, developing into an infructescence of many fruits. Fruits obovate with distinct pointed apex, 5–6 × 2–3 cm, with a thin epicarp covered in smooth, reddish brown scales in vertical rows, each fruit with up to 3 seeds, covered in an edible, white, sweet, sarcotesta, but which is not as good as *S. edulis* Reinw., the cultivated salak.

Distribution and Habitat: Peninsular Malaysia, Sumatra and Borneo (in all states). In shaded lowland, to hill mixed dipterocarp forest, often in wet swampy areas, below 500 m.

Vernacular Names: *salak hutan* (Malay); *ridan* (Iban); *sungsung* (Brunei); *salak habang* (Kalimantan); snake fruit (English).

Notes: This is one of several edible wild *Salacca* species found in Borneo, and it is also commonly cultivated, its fruits often sold in markets. It is sometimes planted in a hedge to form a protective fence with its spiny fronds.

Canarium megalanthum Merr.

Family Burseraceae

橄
榄
科

大
花
橄
榄

Description: A dioecious tree to 35–40 m, bole to 5 m, sometimes with buttresses. Leaves pinnate, with petiole-rachis to c. 30–40 cm, the base of petiole with sub-persistent deeply-lobed stipules, 3–4 lobes to 2 cm tall. Leaflets 3–4–5 pairs, opposite, with a terminal leaflet, petiolules 1–1.5 cm long, pubescent, blades lanceolate to oblong, 8–20 × 4–8 cm, apex gradually acute to acuminate, base cuneate to obtuse, margin entire. Upper surface becoming glabrous, with flat midvein and raised laterals, lower surface with raised veins, pubescent to glabrous, with 10–15 pairs of lateral veins. Inflorescence with the male and female on separate trees, pseudo-terminal in axils of leaves to terminal, narrowly paniculate, with pubescent flowers, male inflorescences to 30 cm long, female to 25 cm forming an infructescence with 4–5 fruits. Fruit a drupe, ellipsoid, 5–7.5 × 3.5–4.5 cm, like a small mango, with green, glabrous to scurfy epicarp to 1–2 mm thick, edible mesocarp to 1 cm thick, white to yellow surrounding a single spindle-shaped brown seed, with a woody, triangular endocarp 2–3 mm thick, the edible white kernel c. 1 cm diameter. The seed with 3 locules, but usually only 1 locule develops a seed.

Distribution and Habitat: Peninsular Malaysia, Sumatra and Borneo. In lowland and hill mixed dipterocarp forest to 360 m. Cultivated for its fruits in Brunei, and the nuts are sold in the market.

Vernacular Names: *rarawa damar* (Malay); *meritus* (Brunei).

Notes: The fruits are the largest in the genus, with a white to yellow, fibrous-looking mesocarp. If eaten, the mesocarp fibres 'melt' in one's saliva—this fact is little known. The trees produce a lot of resin.

Canarium odontophyllum Miq.

Description: Dioecious tree to 35 m tall, bole to 7 m, with buttresses. Leaves pinnate with 3–8 pairs of leaflets, and a terminal leaflet, petioles with distinct basal stipules with toothed lobes, petiole and rachis varying to 25 cm, pubescent. Leaflets with pubescent petiolules, 1–1.5 cm, blades long lanceolate to oblong, 9–28 × 4–11 cm, apex long acuminate, base cuneate to obtuse, margin serrate. Upper surface glabrous, midvein slightly prominent above with hairs, secondary veins slightly sunken above, lower surface densely pubescent, veins prominent with 12–28 pairs of lateral veins. Inflorescences from pseudo-terminal leaf axils, male and female tomentose panicles on different trees, males with many yellow or white flowers on panicles to 50 cm, females with fewer flowers, forming a branching infructescence, 35 cm tall with up to 40 ellipsoid to ovoid fruits. Fruit a drupe, 2.5–4 × 1.7–2.5 cm, immature fruits white, turning to dark blackish purple when ripe, with a saucer-shaped basal calyx and pointed apex. Epicarp thin, to 1 mm, mesocarp 3–7 mm, yellow, oily, edible. Seeds triangular in cross-section with woody endocarp with 3 locules but only one with an edible kernel.

Distribution and Habitat: Sumatra, Borneo and Philippines (Palawan only). Widely cultivated in Brunei and Sarawak. In lowland and hill mixed dipterocarp forest to 500 m.

Vernacular Names: *kembayau* (Malay); *dabai* (Iban); tropical olive, Sibu olive, Brunei olive (English).

Notes: The fruits are edible after being placed in hot water. The oily mesocarp is like an olive, and is considered a delicacy. The fruits are eaten as a side dish, often with salt, sugar or soya sauce. In the cracked nuts, the kernels are edible and taste like almonds. Selected clones are cultivated. The fruits are commonly sold in markets.

Dacryodes rostrata (Blume) H.J. Lam

Description: Medium to large dioecious tree, 25–45 m, bole 5–15 m, with small buttresses. Leaves alternate pinnate with 2–8 pairs of opposite leaflets, petioles and rachis 6–15–25 cm, with no stipules or terminal leaflet. Leaflets with petiolules 1–2 cm with apical and basal pulvinus. Leaflet blades ovate to oblong, 8–30 × 3.5–11 cm, apex long acuminate to 2 cm, base asymmetric, cuneate to obtuse, margins entire. Surfaces glabrous with veins raised on both surfaces, with 5–15 pairs of lateral veins. Inflorescences panicles, pseudo-terminal on twigs or in leaf axils to 35 cm long, with branches to 3 cm, with densely hairy male and female flowers on separate trees. Infructescence with many ovoid to oblong fruits. Fruit a drupe, 2–3.5 × 1 cm, with white latex, immature fruits yellow, ripening to blackish purple. Thin epicarp to 1 mm with white to cream, oily, edible mesocarp surrounding a single seed, round in cross-section, with white edible kernel.

Distribution and Habitat: Indochina, Peninsular Malaysia, Sumatra, Borneo, Philippines and North Sulawesi. Common in lowland and hill mixed dipterocarp forest and secondary forest to 800 m. Sometimes cultivated.
Vernacular Names: *kedondong* (Malay); *seladah* (Iban); *kambayau* (Sabah); *pinanasan* (Brunei).
Notes: Two forms, *f. rostrata* and *f. cuspidata*, are recognised. The former is common and widespread in Sabah and Sarawak and often confused with *dabai* (*Canarium odontophyllum* Miq.), but differs in having no stipules nor terminal leaflet. The mesocarp is made into a relish and eaten with sugar. The fruit, like *dabai*, is put into hot water for 10 minutes before eating. The fruit is also pickled in salt or soya sauce.

Garcinia forbesii King

Description: Small to medium understorey, dioecious tree, 7–10(–15) m tall, bole 1–6 m, fluted at base, with yellow latex. Leaves simple, opposite in a lateral plane, petioles 1–2.5 cm long, base clasping the stem, flat on top, no stipules. Blades variable in size, elliptic-lanceolate to oblanceolate, 7–20 × 5–10 cm, thin, leathery, apex acuminate, 1–2.5 cm long, base cuneate. Both surfaces glabrous, veins slightly raised on both surfaces, with 11–14 pairs of lateral veins, margin entire. Flowers with male flowers in clusters on twig, pedicels to 3 mm, 1–3 female flowers, with short pedicels or sessile. Flowers with 4 petals that are white and pink to red, and open at night, with a foetid odour. Fruit a globose fleshy berry, pointed apically, 2.5–5 cm diameter, ripening from green to pale yellowish to rose red, sub-sessile, pedicel (stalk) 3 mm, with 4 small persistent calyx lobes at the base and an apical, round, papillose, pale brown stigma. Epicarp cream to red, to 5 mm thick, surrounding segments of edible, juicy white pulp (arillode) with 1 or 2 seeds that is considered delicious, and tastes sweet with a fruity aroma.

Distribution and Habitat: Peninsular Malaysia, Sumatra and Borneo. Mixed lowland and hill dipterocarp forest to lower montane forest, also in limestone forest.

Vernacular Names: *kandis hutan* (Malay); Brunei cherry or *asam auraur* (Brunei); *kundong* (Iban); *takob akob* (Sabah); *arui arui* (general); rose kandis (English).

Notes: This species has often been wrongly identified as *G. parvifolia* (Miq.) Miq. It is widely cultivated, and the fruit rinds are dried and sold in markets, for use in cooking as a condiment with fish, curries, and other dishes, more or less as a substitute for tamarind (opposite inset).

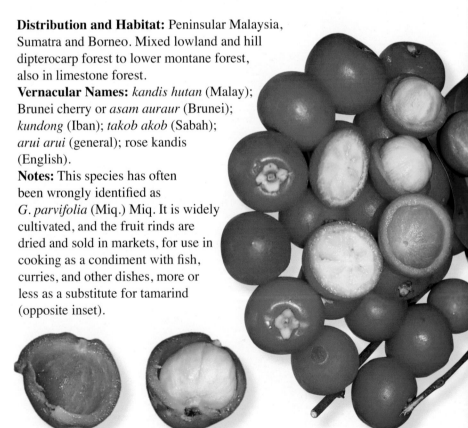

Garcinia hombroniana Pierre

Description: Coastal to understorey dioecious tree, usually 6–10–18 m, bole 2–5 m, often with small buttresses, with white latex in all parts. Leaves simple, opposite, arranged in a lateral plane, petioles 1–1.5 cm, glabrous, base clasping the stem. Blade ovate-elliptic to oblong, 7–20 × 3–7 cm, very variable on the same twig, apex acuminate, base cuneate to obtuse, upper surface glabrous, midvein slightly raised, lateral veins flat, indistinct, lower surface glabrous, midvein prominent, lateral veins flat, indistinct and to over 20 pairs, margin entire. Inflorescence on male trees along apical part of stem, in cymes of 1–4 flowers in a cluster, each flower to 2.5 cm diameter, with 4 white petals; on female trees, flowers single, some in leaf axils, with 4 yellowish petals. Fruit a globose, woody, berry, 4 cm diameter, not splitting open, with persistent calyx lobes, pedicel 0.5–1 cm, and persistent apical, prominent, brown stigma. Epicarp rose red, when ripe, woody, to 5 mm thick, reddish, enclosing 1 or more seeds in a translucent white, juicy, edible pulp (arillode), which is sour with a peach-like flavour.

Distribution and Habitat: Peninsular Malaysia, Indonesia, Borneo, southern Philippines to Nicobar Islands. Common on coastal islands, in sandy seashore habitats and hillsides near the coast. Sometimes cultivated.

Vernacular Names: *beruas* (Malay); *luli* (Brunei); seashore mangosteen (English).

Notes: This is a species closely related to the popular *G. mangostana* L., but without the delicious, sweet, white pulp and it is thus often referred to as *manggis hutan* or wild mangosteen. The fruits are harvested and eaten fresh.

Garcinia mangostana L.

Description: An understorey dioecious tree, 5–25 m tall with a short bole 1–2 m, normally without buttresses, with sticky yellow latex in all parts. Leaves simple, opposite, in a lateral plane on the twig, petioles to 1 cm, the base enclosing the stem. Blade elliptic to oblong, 15–25 × 7–13 cm, soft and leathery, apex cuspidate, base cuneate to obtuse, both surfaces glabrous, with prominent midvein and many closely and evenly spaced, faintly visible pairs of lateral veins. Female flowers single to two on a cyme, at the apical part of the twig. Flowers with four white to yellowish petals. Fruit a globose, woody berry 4–7 cm across, with a short pedicel (stalk) c. 5 mm, with a smooth, dark purple epicarp to 0.9 cm thick, with 4 large persistent calyx lobes (sepals) at the base, and a prominent brown apical stigma. The white pulp (arillode) forms up to 7 segments, 2–3 of which contain fully developed asexual seeds (formed without pollination). The juicy, edible, sweet arillode is delicious.

Distribution and Habitat: Widely cultivated all over Southeast Asia, but generally known as being wild in Sarawak and Sabah, with one report of a male tree. Wild trees were reported for lowland mixed dipterocarp forest in flood plains, and in many such areas the forest has been cleared for agriculture. However, there is some doubt as to it being a truly wild species.

Vernacular Names: *manggis* (Malay); *sikup* (Iban); mangosteen (English).

Notes: In the world of tropical edible fruits, the mangosteen is acknowledged as the 'Queen of Fruits' for its delicious edible arillode, whereas the durian is called the 'King of Fruits'. The fruit 'shell' produces a black dye and is also using in tanning.

Garcinia microcarpa Pierre

Description: Understorey, dioecious trees, usually 10–20 m tall, bole 5–10 m, with yellowish latex (but white latex from fruit pericarp). Leaves simple, oppositely arranged in lateral plane, petioles 2–2.5 cm, grooved above. Blade ovate-elliptic, 12–18 × 6–8 cm, variable on the same twig, apex acuminate to 1.5 cm, base cuneate to rounded, both surfaces glabrous, midvein and lateral veins depressed on upper surface but prominent on lower surface, margin entire. Inflorescences along branches. Fruit a globose berry, 3–3.5 × 2.3–2.5 cm, calyx bracts 5 × 3 mm, pedicel very short, and a persistent, apical, brown stigma which is papillose. The epicarp (fruit wall) thin, greenish with pale brown patches, with white latex, enclosing 6–8 thin, cream coloured seeds, c. 2.5 × 1.3 cm × 2 mm, covered in a translucent, 4 mm thick, edible arillode which is sweet and juicy.

Distribution and Habitat: Borneo only. Lowland and hill mixed dipterocarp forest in Sabah and Sarawak, 30–900 m.
Vernacular Names: *kandis hutan* (Malay).
Notes: The taxonomy of *Garcinia* species in Borneo is very confused, with probably about 60 species recorded and some still undescribed. This species is uncommon to rare.

Garcinia nitida Pierre

Description: Understorey dioecious tree to 30 m, bole 2–6 m with small fluted buttress 0.5 m tall, latex cream-coloured. Leaves simple, opposite, petioles 5–10 mm, grooved. Blade elliptic to lanceolate, 6–10 × 3–4 cm, thin leathery, apex long acuminate, base cuneate. Upper surface glabrous, midvein raised at the base, the rest and the lateral veins flat, lower surface glabrous, midvein raised, lateral veins flat and 7–9 pairs. Male flowers in clusters, females solitary, on the twigs between or below the leaves, with four white to cream spreading petals. Fruit a fleshy, oval-shaped berry with a distinct nipple-shaped apex with a minute, brown stigma, the base of the fruit with 4 small, yellowish, persistent calyx lobes, the berry 3–4 × 2.5–3 cm, green, ripening from yellow to pale orange, with a pulpy, soft, edible epicarp (rind) enclosing light brown seeds 2 × 0.5 × 0.3 cm, which are covered in an edible, translucent, sour pulp (arillode).

Distribution and Habitat: Endemic to Borneo. In lowland and hill mixed dipterocarp forest to 900 m. Uncommon in cultivation.

Vernacular Names: *kandis hutan* (Malay).

Notes: This species has been confused with the yellow to orange fruited *G. parvifolia* (Miq.) Miq., also called *kandis*, which has the apical stigma of the fruit concealed in a sunken pit. The sour rind and pulp of the fruit are used as condiments in cooking (a substitute for tamarind), with rice, fish, or curries. They are sometimes also used to make jam or drinks with sugar added.

Family Clusiaceae

藤黄科

樱桃山竹

Garcinia parvifolia (Miq.) Miq.

Description: Small to medium, understorey, dioecious tree, 7–25 m (rarely 30 m), bole 2–15 m, some fluted near the base, with yellow latex. Leaves simple, opposite in a lateral plane, petioles 0.7–1.3 cm, twisted, but flat on upper surface, true stipules lacking. Blades very variable even on the same twig, usually smaller on tall trees, elliptic to lanceolate-elliptic, 5–18 × 2.5–6 cm, sometimes asymmetric, thin, leathery, apex acuminate to 1–2 cm, base cuneate to obtuse. Both surfaces glabrous, veins on upper surface flat, prominent below, with 8–10 pairs of lateral veins, margin entire. Male flowers grouped in clusters along twig, with pale yellow petals, on pedicels to 1 cm, with unusual scent at night. Female flowers larger, on shorter pedicels, with pale yellow petals, on twigs behind the leaves. Fruit a globose to ovoid fleshy berry that varies in size on the same twig, green, ripening yellow to orange, 2.5 × 2–3.5 × 3 cm, pedicel (stalk) 5–6 mm, with small calyx lobes, sunken at base, and small apical stigma, sunken and often concealed in a pit. The thin (0.5 mm) epicarp (rind) is pulpy pale orange, with a translucent, juicy arillode which is usually sour, and 2 or more seeds to 1.5 cm long × 5 mm × 3 mm.

Distribution and Habitat: Peninsular Malaysia, Sumatra and Borneo. Widely distributed in Borneo but uncommon and only sometimes cultivated. In mixed lowland dipterocarp forest, also recorded in swamp forest, heath forest, and on limestone, to 600 m altitude.

Vernacular Names: *kandis* (Malay); *kedui* or *lulai* (Iban).

Notes: In Peninsular Malaysia, trees of this species have narrowly elliptic leaves. The botanical name, *G. parvifolia*, has often been wrongly applied to the rose kandis (*G. forbesii* King). Sweeter forms of this species are eaten fresh, usually as a condiment in cooking rice or fish.

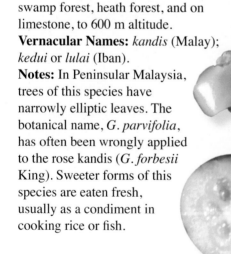

Terminalia catappa L.

Family Combretaceae

使君子科 榄仁树

Description: Medium tree to 25 m tall, the bole often leaning (on seashores), to 5 m, with small buttresses, the large spreading crown formed by whorls of lateral branches. Deciduous for a short period. Leaves usually spirally-arranged in whorls at the ends of twigs, petioles 1–2.5 cm without stipules, blades obovate, tapering to a narrow base, leathery, 25–30 × 6–18 cm, with 9–12 pairs of veins. Inflorescences short, terminal raceme with greenish white to cream flowers. Fruit an ellipsoid drupe with distinct flattened edges 2–3 mm wide, ripening from green to yellow, 4–6 × 2.5–4 × 2.5–3 cm, the soft outer epicarp to 4 mm thick, covering a fibrous mesocarp to 8 mm thick, with the ellipsoid, edible white kernel to 3 cm long and 6–7 mm thick.

Distribution and Habitat: Oceania and Southeast Asia. Cultivated throughout the tropics. Grows commonly along seashores, and coastal forests, and disturbed land to 300 m.

Vernacular Names: *ketapang* (Malay); *ketapang pantai* (Indonesia); umbrella tree & tropical almond (English).

Notes: The fruit kernels are often eaten by school children. The fibrous fruit is difficult to open to extract the kernel, which can be eaten raw, but is better roasted. The fibrous fruits float, and are distributed by sea currents, but can also be spread inland by bats that feed on the mesocarp. This species is cultivated in the Pacific Islands, where selected varieties have much larger fruits and kernels. The tree is commonly planted as a shade tree. Two other Bornean species have edible fruits. *T. copelandii* Elm and *T. microcarpa* Decre (Syn. *T. edulis* F. Muell.).

Alangium javanicum (Blume) Wangerin

Description: Small to medium-sized tree, 8–20(–30) m, bole 3–5 m, often with flying buttresses (with a gap between the base of the buttress and the ground). Leaves simple, alternate in a lateral plane, upper surface glabrous, lower surface sometimes with velvety hairs, petioles thickened, 0.5 cm–3 cm, blades ovate-elliptic to obovate, 8–15(–30) × 4–6(–10) cm, apex acute to acuminate, base obtuse to rounded, pinnately-veined, with 6–10(–20) pairs of lateral veins. Inflorescences with 1–3 short branches and 2–30 flowers in a cyme, often from leaf axils, with white tubular flowers. Fruit ellipsoid to 1.5–2 cm long by 7–9 mm diameter, with a persistent calyx. Epicarp thin, glabrous, pink to purple when ripe, with a translucent white mesocarp which is sweet and edible, and a pale brown seed, 10 × 3–4 mm.

Distribution and Habitat: Java, Sumatra and Borneo. Widely distributed as an understorey tree in lowland and hill dipterocarp forest, and less common in lower montane forest to 1600 m.

Vernacular Names: *wangerin*, *satu inchi*, *kondolon* (Malay).

Notes: Several distinct varieties of *A. javanicum* were once recognised, but it now forms a complex of species with *A. ebenaceum* (C.B. Clarke) Harms, which is also widespread in Borneo and likewise has edible fruits. All species in this complex have entire leaves with pinnate veins. The irregular fruiting of this species means that it is rarely cultivated, and it is mainly a forest product.

Shorea macrophylla (de Vriese) P.S. Ashton

Family Dipterocarpaceae　龙脑香科　大叶娑罗双

Description: Tree to 45 m, bole c. 15 m, buttresses to 2 m tall. Leaves simple, alternate, stipules to 5 cm, petioles 1.5–3 cm, sometimes with pulvinus, glabrous. Blade elliptic-oblong, 17–35 × 10–14 cm, apex acuminate, base obtuse or subcordate, margin entire. Upper surface glabrous, midvein and laterals flat, lower surface with prominent, glabrous veins, lateral veins 11–20 pairs. Inflorescence a panicle, terminal and axillary in leaf axils to 17 cm, with pale pink flowers. Fruit a nut, with 3 long and 2 shorter calyx lobes, 11 × 3 and 8 × 1.5 cm, nut obovoid, 6 × 4 cm, with glabrous, smooth epicarp and endocarp, enclosing the kernel which is rich in edible vegetable oil.

Distribution and Habitat: Endemic to Borneo. In mixed dipterocarp forest especially in flood plains and along rivers, less common on hill sides to 600 m. Commonly cultivated, with selected cultivars often planted in community forests.

Vernacular Names: *kawang jantung* (general); *engkabang jantong* (Iban); illipe nut (English).

Notes: Trees commonly fruit in masting years (often 5–7 years apart), and this is when the fruits are collected, processed, and often exported for use as a cooking oil (with a high melting point), cocoa butter substitute, and for lipsticks. It was a common source of cooking oil prior to the readily available palm oil today. Several other dipterocarp species in the genus *Shorea* have similarly edible kernels, such as *S. splendida* (de Vries) P.S. Ashton.

Elateriospermum tapos Blume

Family Euphorbiaceae

大戟科

豆桐

Description: A shortly deciduous, mid-canopy monoecious tree to 35 m, bole to 10–15 m, fluted, sometimes with short buttresses, with sticky white latex in bark, leaves and panicles. Leaves simple, spirally arranged, with small stipules, petioles 4–5 cm, grooved, with proximal pulvinus and 2 glands at the base of the leaf. The tree drops all its leaves for a short period, producing a new flush of red juvenile leaves at the same time as when it comes into flower. Blade elliptic to oblong to oblanceolate, 8–23 × 3–8 cm, apex acuminate, base cuneate to obtuse, margin entire, upper surface glabrous, midvein and lateral veins flat, lower surface glabrous, veins prominent with 8–12 pairs of lateral veins. Inflorescences sub-terminal to terminal panicles, in leaf axils, to 17 cm long, with both male and female yellowish-cream flowers and with a nasty fragrance. Each cyme of the inflorescence has a central female flower. Fruit oblong, 4–5 cm, a dehiscent capsule, with 3 locules and a thin hard epicarp and mesocarp to 3 mm thick, greenish-yellow and flushed pinkish or red when ripe, turning brown. Fruit hanging on 4 cm long pedicel. Seeds oblong, dark brown, 3–4 × 1 cm with no aril.

Distribution and Habitat: Southern Thailand, Peninsular Malaysia, Sumatra, Java and Borneo. It is found in lowland and hill mixed dipterocarp forest, and secondary forest to 600 m. Seldom cultivated.

Vernacular Names: *perah* (Malay); *kelampai* (Iban); *pogoh nut* (Sabah).

Notes: This is a popular fruit, and the roasted seeds are commonly sold in roadside stalls, especially in Thailand. The kernels of the seeds have to be boiled and roasted before they are eaten, as they contain poisonous hydrocyanides. The seeds are also pickled in salt, or fermented into a paste, or the oil is extracted for cooking. The ripe fruits fall to the ground and are usually collected from trees in the forest.

Archidendron jiringa (Jack) I.C.Nielsen

Description: Tree to 25 m, bole up to 10 m, with a large rounded crown. Leaves pinnate with 2–3 pairs of leaflets, petioles with rachis to 48 cm, leaflets glabrous, greenish-yellow, oblong elliptic, 5–28 × 3–10 cm. Inflorescences panicles, 10–20 cm, from leaf axils, with clusters of fluffy cream flowers. Fruit a legume, seed pod 20–25 cm long and 3–4 cm wide, with 3–6 seeds, twisted into a spiral, with distinct segments for each seed, purplish brown with thick leathery epicarp. Seeds flattened, roundish, greenish-white, 3–4 cm diameter, with unpleasant garlic-like smell.

Distribution and Habitat: Bangladesh, Myanmar, Thailand, Peninsular Malaysia, Indonesia and Borneo. Lowland coastal forest, and often found in secondary forest. Commonly cultivated in Borneo.

Vernacular Names: *jering* or *jaring* (Malay and Iban); dog fruit or black head (English).

Notes: The pods and seeds are commonly sold in the local markets in Borneo. The seeds are rich in protein, and have curative properties for diabetes. The young seeds are edible raw, but the mature seeds contain djenkolic acid and are usually boiled, with the water changed three times, which also removes the unpleasant smell. The seeds are often fried and eaten with salt and grated coconut. There is some doubt if this species is truly native to Borneo.

Dialium indum L.

Description: Tree 20–50 m, bole c. 5–25 m with narrow buttresses. Leaves compound, pinnate, with 3–6 rows of glabrous leaflets. Petiole and rachis 12–20 cm long, small stipules present at base, leaflets alternate in a lateral plane with a terminal leaflet, petiolules 5–10 mm, blade ovate-lanceolate to elliptic, 6–15 × 3–5 cm, base obtuse, apex acuminate. Inflorescences terminal and from leaf axils, panicles 10–20 cm long, with many small, fragrant white flowers. The fruit is a small oval pod, with a brittle, dry, thin shell-like epicarp, velvety black when ripe, 1.5–2.2 cm long, slightly compressed, with a squarish seed to 1 cm diameter, covered in a thin, brown to orange aril which is sweet or sour.

Distribution and Habitat: Peninsular Malaysia, Sumatra, Java and Borneo. In lowland mixed dipterocarp forest to hill forest to 300 m.
Vernacular Names: *keranji* (Malay); *keranji paya* (Sarawak & Sabah); velvet tamarind (English).
Notes: The fruits are often sold in local markets, and occasionally planted around villages, as it also has a timber that makes good tool handles. At one period there was a regional trade in the fruits from Sumatra.

Parkia speciosa Hassk.

Description: Tree 30–50 m, bole 20 m with buttresses. Leaves bipinnate, petioles with proximal pulvinus, brown rachis 15–30 cm long, with 10–18 pairs of side stalks each 5–6 cm long, pubescent, with brown petiolules 2–3 mm, each side stalk with 20–35 pairs of small, sessile, linear-lanceolate leaflets, 5–7 × 2–4 mm, with rounded apex and base. Inflorescences usually terminal on twigs, with pendulous peduncle 16–20 cm long, inflorescence 7 cm long with small creamy white flowers, producing nectar which smells like durian and attracts bat pollinators. The peduncle then extends to 25–30 cm, usually with a cluster of 6–18 legume pods, each flattened, slightly twisted, 30–40 cm long, 3.5–5 cm wide (pedicels 6–8 cm long), swollen at the seeds. Each pod contains 10–15 oval-shaped seeds with a thin green testa (endocarp). Seeds white and 3 × 1.5 cm.

Distribution and Habitat: Peninsular Malaysia, southern Thailand, Indonesia and Borneo. Scattered in lowland and hill forests to 800 m. Often cultivated in villages.
Vernacular Names: *petai* (Malay and Iban); twisted cluster bean or bitter bean (English).
Notes: The pods are usually harvested from forest trees and whole pods or the seeds are sold in markets all over Borneo. Both the young pods and seeds are cooked as a vegetable, or the seeds are cooked with rice.

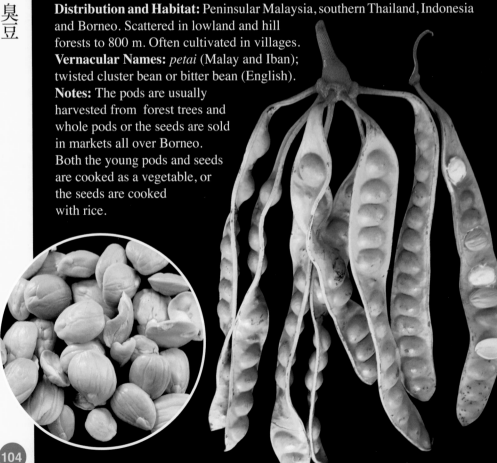

Castanopsis hypophoenicea (Seemen) Soepadmo

Description: Tree to 30 m tall, monoecious, bole 7–10 m, buttresses not seen. Leaves simple, spirally arranged, petioles 7–17 mm, pubescent, with basal pulvinus, stipules to 6–8 × 4–5 mm. Blade elliptic to oblong, 10–17 × 4–7 cm, apex acuminate to 15 mm, base rounded to acute, asymmetric, margin entire, upper surface glabrous, midvein and lateral veins impressed above, lower surface pubescent, veins prominent with 11–12 pairs of lateral veins. Inflorescences in spikes 8–11 cm long, of male or female flowers, or mixed. Male flowers in clusters of 3–5 flowers along rachis, female flowers single along rachis. Fruit a cupule, subsessile on rachis, ovoid to ellipsoid, 7–11 × 6–8 cm, the epicarp 5 mm thick, covered in slender, branched, straight to curved spines, 10–22 mm long, arranged irregularly over the surface, with spaces between them. Nuts 1 in each cupule, splitting open into 2–4 locules. Nuts ovoid to ellipsoid, 6–7 × 4–4.5 cm, with a glabrous, thick woody endocarp 4–5 mm thick, filled by the white edible kernel, to 4 × 3 cm, adnate to the cupule.

Distribution and Habitat: Endemic to Borneo. In primary and secondary mixed hill dipterocarp forest to 800 m, widely distributed throughout Borneo.
Vernacular Names: *berangan* (Malay); *berangan bo* (Iban); chestnut (English).
Notes: The nuts must be boiled or roasted before eating. It is one of two species of large edible chestnuts with a single kernel compared to several species that have 2–3 smaller nuts per cupule such as *C. foxworthyi* Schottky and *C. costata* (Blume) A. DC. This species has larger cupules and nuts than *C. megacarpa* Gamble.

Castanopsis megacarpa Gamble

Family Fagaceae

壳斗科　大果锥

Description: Tree to 36 m tall, monoecious, bole to 15 m, sometimes with buttresses to 2 m. Leaves simple, spirally arranged, petioles 1–2.5 cm with basal pulvinus, stipules present to 5 × 2 mm. Blade lanceolate-oblong to elliptic-oblong, 13–22(–30) × 5–7(–10) cm, apex acute, base cuneate to obtuse (lower montane trees have smaller leaves). Upper surface glabrous, midvein slightly raised, lateral veins flat, lower surface pubescent with prominent veins and 13–15 pairs of lateral veins. Inflorescence with flowers male or female, terminal or subterminal from leaf axils, in spikes, male inflorescence 6–17 cm, rachis with clusters of 3 flowers, female inflorescence 9–12 cm with solitary flowers along the rachis. Fruit a cupule, sessile on rachis, ellipsoid to globose, 5–8 × 3–5.5 cm, pubescent and densely spiny, spines 15–20 mm long and branched, irregularly arranged. Seed a single nut per cupule, ellipsoid to globose, 3–7 × 3–5.5 cm with a thick woody endocarp (shell) 4–5 mm thick, kernel edible after roasting in the ashes of fires, reportedly poisonous if eaten raw.

Distribution and Habitat: Peninsular Malaysia, Singapore and Borneo. In primary lowland to hill mixed dipterocarp forest and kerangas forest. Also in lower montane forest to 1400 m.

Vernacular Names: *berangan* (Malay); *berangan entadu* (Iban); chestnut (English).

Notes: In Peninsular Malaysia, this species is called *berangan tangga*, indicating it is poisonous if not roasted. It is one of the few edible species found in lowland forest, and is similar to *C. hypophoenicea* (Seemen) Soepadmo, which is also an edible species with a single large nut per cupule. *C. endertii* Hatus. ex Soepadmo is a montane species with a single edible nut per cupule.

Gnetum gnemon L.

Description: Understorey dioecious tree to 10–15 m tall, bole straight with distinct raised rings, with whorls of branches from the base, sometimes a clear bole to c. 2 m in older trees. Leaves simple, opposite, petioles 0.5–1.7 cm, blades elliptic to obovate or broadly lanceolate, 7.5–22 × 2.5–10 cm, apex acuminate, base cuneate, margin entire, undulating, both surfaces glabrous with veins flat above, prominent below, c. 9 pairs of lateral veins. Inflorescence 1–3, from leaf axils or on branches, a spike 3–6(–12) cm long, with strobili in whorls at the nodes, male greenish white, female strobili 5–8 at a node, globose. 'Fruit' drupe-like, ellipsoid, 1–3.5 cm long, more or less sessile, strobili subtended by fleshy collars which are yellow turning to orange or red when ripe. The seed covered in a tough, thin epicarp and mesocarp that is edible, with a thin hard endocarp less than 1 mm thick.

Distribution and Habitat: Native in the Philippines, Sulawesi, Borneo to New Guinea. In Borneo, an understorey tree on offshore islands, or in hill mixed dipterocarp forest in Sarawak to 1000 m, where the Iban distinguish wild species from selected cultivated ones. Selected cultivars are commonly planted in villages, and the young leaves and fruits sold in markets. At least two varieties of *G. gnemon* are recorded for Borneo (var. *brunonianum* (Griff.) Markgr. and var. *tenerum* Markgr.), and many other species are still unnamed.

Vernacular Names: *meninjau* (Malay); *sabong* or *sabung arau* (Iban); *melindjo* (Indonesian).

Notes: It is best known for the crisps or crackers called kerupuk prepared from the ground, dried kernels cooked in coconut oil. The fruits and kernels can be eaten raw, but are usually cooked or roasted. The young leaves, inflorescences and fruits are also cooked together with vegetables.

Molineria latifolia (Dryand. ex W.T. Aiton) Herb. ex Kurz

Family Hypoxidaceae

仙茅科

仙蜜果

Description: Perennial herb, stemless, forming a clump of erect leaves surrounded at the base by several inflorescences. Several individuals can form a small patch of plants, but mostly they occur singly. Plants often less than 1 m tall in sunny open areas, but in shaded forest to 2 m tall, with 7–10 leaves to 150 cm, petioles to 100 cm, the mid-section conduplicate (U-shaped), 6–10 mm diameter × 1.5 cm thick. Blade 60–150 × 8–25 cm, elliptic-lanceolate, apex long-acuminate, base long-cuneate, plicate, with parallel veins, 8–10 on each side of the midvein, upper surface glabrous, pubescent below, margin entire and with hairs. Inflorescence to 10 cm tall from the base of leaves, a compact panicle-like head, to 8 cm diameter, with many green bracts and yellow flowers. Fruit an ovoid to oblong berry, with narrow wing along side, pedicel 2–3 cm long, berry 2–3 cm long × 1.2–1.7 cm diameter. The epicarp ripening white tinged pink, 1 mm thick, with mesocarp enclosing small, black seeds less than 1 mm long, with white aril-like pulp that is eaten together with the seeds and is sweet and juicy, tasting like dragon fruit.

Distribution and Habitat: Throughout Malesia. Lowland and hill mixed dipterocarp forest to lower montane forest, heath forest, secondary forest and disturbed lands. Commonly found around villages.

Vernacular Names: *lamba* (Sabah); *lemba babi* (Iban); *tambaka* (general).

Notes: This species can be confused with other species in the same family that also have edible fruits and leaves which can be used to produce fibres to make strings.

Litsea garciae S. Vidal

Family Lauraceae

樟科

兰屿木姜子

Description: Medium-sized, understorey, dioecious tree 10–30 m (rarely 40 m), bole 5–10 m with short buttresses c. 1 m. Leaves simple, alternate, or in whorls on twigs, petioles 1–2(–3) cm, grooved, without stipules, blade ovate to lanceolate to oblanceolate, 12–30(–50) × 5–10(–15) cm, apex acute to acuminate, base cuneate to obtuse, margin entire, upper surface glabrous, midvein and lateral veins flat to sunken, lower surface glabrous, with 12–22 pairs of prominent lateral veins. Male and female inflorescences between leaves or along branches (ramiflorous), and sometimes cauliflorous on the upper bole. Inflorescences single or in clusters of 2–3, from 2–3(–6) cm long with short branches, flowers white, male flowers with orange anthers. 1–6 fruits usually produced per inflorescence, with pedicels to 1 cm. Fruit a single seeded berry sitting in a green cupule formed by the true receptacle, with a thickened stalk 1 cm long at the end of the pedicel, and ripening from white to pale pink to red. The berry oblate in shape, 3–4(–5) cm diameter and 3–4 cm long, the epicarp to 3 mm thick, with a single large brown seed, surrounded by a soft, edible, greenish-white pulp that tastes like avocado.

Distribution and Habitat: Philippines and Borneo. In lowland to hill mixed dipterocarp forest, sometimes in swampy and secondary forest, to 800 m. A popular fruit tree and often cultivated from seeds in Kalimantan and Sarawak. Female trees can be propagated by marcots.

Vernacular Names: *engkala* (Malay & Iban); *pengoloban* (Sabah); *kalang kala* (Indon).

Notes: The fruits are often boiled or left in hot water for 10 minutes before eating. Unripe fruits are also preserved in vinegar or salt solution.

114

Sonneratia caseolaris (L.) Engl.

Description: Medium-sized tree, 8–20 m tall, bole 3–5 m, often leaning over from the river bank, with pendulous young branches in an open crown. It produces a dense mass of pointed breathing roots (pneumatophores) on the tidal mud banks. Leaves simple, opposite, petioles without stipules and 7–11 mm long. Blade elliptic to elliptic-ovate, 3.8–9.5 × 2–8 cm, apex acute to blunt, base cuneate, margin entire, surfaces glabrous, veins flat, not easily visible, 8–12 pairs of lateral veins. Inflorescence a terminal corymb or cluster of 2–3 flowers, with cup-shaped calyx with 6–8 green lobes, the flowers with red petals, and a mass of stamens that have pink bases and are white apically and form a puff ball. Fruit a many-seeded berry, subtended by the persistent calyx with green spreading lobes, round but flattened in shape, 5–7.5 cm diameter and 4 cm long, with green epicarp and prominent, apical, persistent style. The seeds are surrounded by a whitish edible pulp.

Distribution and Habitat: Sri Lanka, through tropical Southeast Asia, Borneo, New Guinea, northern Australia and Solomon Islands. Trees are found scattered along the banks of tidal rivers with brackish water, and tidal zones where the mangroves have less saline water.

Vernacular Names: *berembang* (Malay); *perepat* (Sabah); *pedada* (Iban); mangrove crab-apple (English).

Notes: The use of the edible fruits is reported from a wide range of countries. In Borneo, the fruit is now not utilised so much as it was in the past by coastal communities. The young fruits are sour and are used in curries or chutneys. The ripe fruits are eaten raw or are cooked, and have a cheese-like flavour.

Durio crassipes Kosterm. & Soegeng

Description: Tree to 60 m tall, bole up to 20 m with buttresses. Leaves simple, alternate, narrow elliptic, petioles c. 1.5 cm, with distal pulvinus, stipules soon falling off. Blade 7–11 cm long × 2.5–3 cm wide, glabrous above, lower surface covered in brown scales and hairs. Inflorescences in clusters of 10 or more flowers along the branches, with pink to red petals. Capsular fruit ovoid to subglobose, 7–10 × 5.5–7 cm, with 5 mm long red spines. The black seeds to 3 cm long, totally covered in creamy, yellow, sweet, edible aril.

Distribution and Habitat: Endemic to Borneo (Sabah & Sarawak only). In mixed hill forest from 500–700 m.

Vernacular Names: *durian hutan* (Malay).

Notes: This is a very rare species. The fruits open on the branches and are eaten by hornbills and squirrels, so wild trees have to be climbed by humans to get at the fruits. It has potential for breeding and selection.

Durio dulcis Becc.

Description: Tree to 50 m tall, bole up to 20 m, with large buttresses. Leaves simple, alternate, elliptic to oblong, petioles 1–2 cm, with distal pulvinus, stipules soon falling off. Blade 7–16 cm long × 3–6 cm wide, with glabrous glossy upper surface, lower surface covered in pale brown scales and hairs. Inflorescences in clusters of several flowers along branches, with pink to dark pink petals. Capsular fruit globose, 12–15 cm with red spines 1.5–2 cm long with grey tips. Ripe fruits have a very strong odour which can be smelt from more than ½ km away. The fruits drop to the ground, and are eaten by sun bears and porcupines, as they are difficult to open. The dark brown to black seeds to 2–2.5 cm long are partially to fully covered in a thick creamy, white to pale yellow aril, with a sweet to astringent taste (peppermint-like).

Distribution and Habitat: Endemic to Borneo. It is found scattered in mixed lowland dipterocarp forest, to hill forest up to 500 m.
Vernacular Names: *durian tahis*, *durian daun* & *durian merah* (Malay); *tutong* (Iban).
Notes: This species is not commonly cultivated, the fruit being jungle-collected. It has good potential for selection.

Durio grandiflorus (Mast.) Kosterm. & Soegeng

Description: Tree to 30 m, bole to 5 m with buttresses to 3 m. Leaves simple, alternate, ovate to obovate or oblong, petioles with distal pulvinus, 1–3 cm, stipules not observed. Blade 10–30 cm long × 4–13 cm wide, with 11–16 pairs of lateral veins, upper surface glabrous, lower surface covered in pale grey green or pale golden brown scales and hairs (variety *tomentosus* Salma has pale green stellate hairs on the lower surface). Inflorescences cymes with 1–3 small white flowers in leaf axils and along branches (ramiflorous). Capsular fruit ellipsoid, 15–20 × 10–15 cm with bluish green to grey green (rarely yellow), conical spines 10–15 mm long, the fruit valves splitting wide open spreading wide on the tree, displaying the yellow or red arils. The edible aril covers the black or dark brown seeds which are 2–3 cm long.

Distribution and Habitat: Endemic to Borneo, with var. *tomentosus* found in Sarawak only. The Sabah form usually has a red aril.
Vernacular Names: *durian monyet*, *durian hantu* (Malay).
Notes: The aril is thin and is used with chillies in a relish (*tampayak*). The trees have to be climbed to collect the fruits as soon as they open.

Durio graveolens Becc.

Description: Tree to 40–50 m tall, bole up to 25 m with buttresses. Leaves simple, alternate, elliptic to oblong, petioles 2–3 cm long, with distal pulvinus, stipules curved to 2 cm. Blades 10–26 cm long, 4–10 cm wide, with 11–13 pairs of lateral veins, upper surface glabrous, lower surface covered in coppery brown scales and hairs. Inflorescences cymes in clusters of up to 6 white flowers along the branches. Capsular fruit globose to ovoid, 8–18 cm long × 10–15 cm wide, covered in long yellow to orange spines (sometimes green), of 1–2.5 cm. The fruit's valves open on the branches. The glossy brown seeds are 3–5 cm and are covered in a creamy to cheese-like edible aril that varies in colour from cream to yellow to orange-pink or red. The creamy-textured aril usually has no odour, and tastes like avocado.

Distribution and Habitat: Peninsular Malaysia, Sumatra, southern Philippines and Borneo. Widespread in lowland dipterocarp and swampy forest, often in flat land along rivers, but also in hill forest to 300 m and on ridges.

Vernacular Names: *durian kuning* (Sarawak); *durian merah* (Sabah); *rian isa* (Iban).

Notes: This is a popular fruit and is widely cultivated. However, the fruits have to be harvested on the tree just as they open, or as soon as they are ripe. Many forms of this species have an orange to orangey-red aril that has a more cheesy texture and a more durian-like flavour and odour, and these are often called *durian dalit*. Natural hybrids of this species and *D. zibethinus* Murray are common and are often cultivated.

Durio kinabaluensis (Bakh. ex Wyatt-Smith) Kosterm. & Soegeng

Description: Tree to 40 m tall, bole 10–15 m with buttresses. Leaves simple, alternate, elliptic to oblong, petioles 1.5–2 cm long, with distal pulvinus, stipules not seen. Blade 10–16 cm long × 4–6 cm wide, the upper surface glabrous, the lower surface covered in golden brown scales and hairs. The inflorescences form branched cymes or clusters of 5–6 large pink to reddish flowers along the branches. The globose to slightly ovoid, capsular fruits are greenish-yellow to yellow, 8–10 cm in diameter, with some fruits slightly lobed, and with conical spines <1 cm long. The light brown seeds to 3 cm long are covered in a thin, white to cream to pale yellow, sweet, edible aril.

Distribution and Habitat: Endemic to Borneo (Sabah only). In hill forest to upper hill forest and lower montane forest from 800–1300 m.
Vernacular Names: *durian tapuloh* (Sabah).
Notes: It is sometimes planted around villages in the Crocker Range in Sabah, and the fruits are often sold at the roadside stalls.

Durio kutejensis (Hassk.) Becc.

Description: Tree to 20–25 m, short bole with small buttresses and a low branching habit. Leaves simple, alternate, elliptic to oblong, petioles 1.5–3 cm with distal pulvinus, stipules not observed. Blade 20–33 × 6–12 cm, with 14–16(–20) pairs of lateral veins, upper surface glabrous, dark green, lower surface covered in silvery pale green scales. Inflorescences cymes in clusters along branches, 3 or more flowers per cyme, with large flowers with red petals. Capsular fruit globose to ovoid, with five lobes visible, 10–20 cm long × 10–15 cm wide with yellow spines 1–1.5 cm long. The ripe fruits drop to the ground, and the valves then open. Seeds 3–4 cm long with golden-brown testa completely covered in a smooth creamy, yellow to pink or orange, sweet aril.

Distribution and Habitat: Endemic to Borneo. In lowland dipterocarp forest in alluvial valleys, and on the lower slopes of surrounding hills to 300 m.
Vernacular Names: *durian luas* or *tapis*, *durian pulu* (Malay); *rian mekah* (Iban).
Notes: This is a popular fruit commonly cultivated in the rural areas.

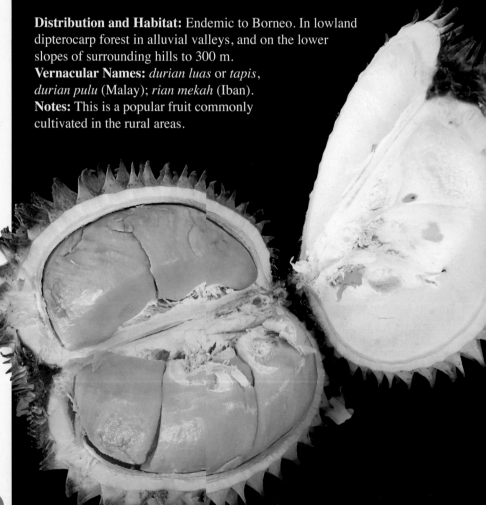

Durio oxleyanus Griff.

Description: Tree to 40–45 m tall, bole up to 30 m, large buttresses. Leaves simple, alternate, ovate-elliptic to oblong to obovate, petioles 2–3 cm long, with distal pulvinus, blades 8–23 cm long × 4–8 cm wide, with 19–22 pairs of lateral veins, upper surface glabrous, lower surface whitish-green with dense stellate hairs, distinguishing this species. Inflorescences cymes with short branches with clusters of 4–10 small white to cream flowers from leaf axils or along ramiflorous branches. Capsular fruit globose, 10–20 cm long and wide, with long curved grey-green to yellowish spines 1–3 cm long. The seeds covered by a thick white to cream or pale yellow sweet aril, covering the golden-brown seeds of 3–4 × 1.5–2 cm.

Distribution and Habitat: Peninsular Malaysia, Sumatra and Borneo (Kalimantan, Sabah and Sarawak). Wet lowland mixed dipterocarp forest to mixed hill forest to 300 m. Commonly cultivated.
Vernacular Names: *durian beludu* (Malay); *durian sukang* (Sabah, Sarawak).
Notes: This species has a very sweet, creamy aril, but the fragrance is less strong compared to *D. zibethinus* Murray. The fruits fall to the ground without splitting and are difficult to open.

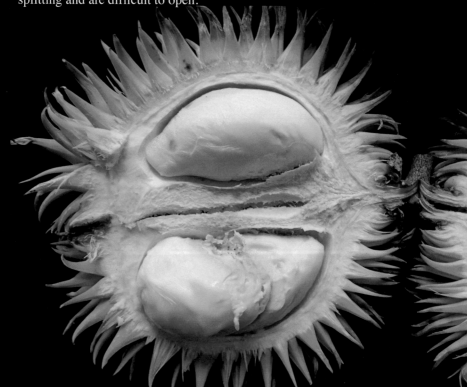

Durio testudinarum Becc.

Description: Tree usually 25 m up to 40–60 m, bole to 10 m, with small buttresses. Leaves simple, alternate, elliptic to oblong, petioles 1.5 cm long, with distal pulvinus, stipules to 2 cm. Blade 10–30 cm long × 3–9 cm wide (var. *crassifolius* Salma having more ovate, leathery leaves with prominent lateral veins), upper surface glabrous, lower surface pale green with scales and hairs. Inflorescences cauliflorous, forming cushions on the bole, often at the base of the tree and forming bosses or knobs on the buttresses, with solitary or clusters of showy white flowers. Fruit capsular with five lobes, globose to ovoid, greenish yellow to yellow to brownish with a long peduncle 6–10 cm, and fruit 15–20 cm long × 10–16 cm wide with conical spines 5–8 mm. Seeds dark brown, 3–4 cm long, are covered in a thin, white to pale yellow, sweet edible aril, with a watery to slightly creamy texture tasting a bit like caramel cream.

Distribution and Habitat: Endemic to Borneo. In lowland forest and swampy forest to hill forest, to 300 m.

Vernacular Names: *durian kura-kura* (Malay); *rian kura-kura* (Iban); tortoise durian (English).

Notes: This unusual durian is often cultivated. The fruits are also consumed by sun bears and mouse deer, which distribute the seeds.

Family Malvaceae

锦葵科

乌龟榴莲

锦葵科　乌龟榴莲

142

Durio zibethinus Murray

Family Malvaceae

锦葵科

榴莲

Description: Tree to 30–50 m tall, bole up to 10 m with short buttresses. Leaves simple, alternate, ovate to elliptic to oblong, petioles 1–2 cm long with distal pulvinus, stipules to 1 cm. Blade 10–20 cm long, 3–6 cm wide, with 9–11 pairs of lateral veins, upper surface glabrous, glossy dark green, lower surface covered in silvery to golden scales and hairs. Inflorescences cymes with branches of several white flowers in clusters, ramiflorous along the branches, open at night, strongly sweet-scented with copious nectar to attract bat pollinators. Capsular fruit globose to ovoid, 15–30 cm long, 10–25 cm diameter, covered in green to brownish spines 1–2 cm long. Fruit with 5 locules, dropping to ground when ripe and the valves then opening. Seeds light brown, 3–5 cm long, covered in a creamy white or greyish white or cream to yellow sweet aril, that has a pungent odour.

Distribution and Habitat: Thailand, Peninsular Malaysia, Sumatra, Borneo, Philippines and New Guinea. Widespread in lowland mixed dipterocarp forest, peat swamp forest, to hill forest in Borneo to 250 m.

Vernacular Names: *durian* (Malay).

Notes: Wild forest trees in Borneo often have fruits with a greyish white aril which is sweet but has a bitter aftertaste, and is still popular locally, and commonly cultivated as a select cultivar. Trees of this species are self-incompatible, so mixed clones have to be planted. It is also cultivated on a commercial scale.

Microcos crassifolia Burrett

Description: Small tree less than 10 m tall, bole less than 1.5 m, with low branching. Leaves simple, alternate in a lateral plane, elliptic to obovate, petioles 3–3.5 cm with distinct distal pulvinus, stipules small and obscure. Blade 10–15–30 cm long × 6–9 cm wide, with 6–7 pairs of lateral veins, surfaces glabrous. Inflorescences branching, 2–9 cm long, terminal or from leaf axils of twigs, with small white or cream flowers. Fruits small, orange, pear-shaped drupes, pedicels 5 mm, drupes 2–2.5 cm long × 1.0–1.5 cm wide, with thin orange epicarp, mesocarp juicy, orange, with orange fibres. Seed with woody endocarp, 8 mm diameter.

Distribution and Habitat: Borneo (Sabah & Sarawak only). Understorey tree in lowland alluvial forest, swamp forest, and often along riverbanks.
Vernacular Names: *chanderai* (Malay);
bunsi (Sarawak).
Notes: The small fruits are chewed
to extract a sweet, tasty juice,
leaving the fibres and seed.
It is rarely cultivated. Other
Bornean species are
poorly known.

Sterculia foetida L.

Description: Deciduous tree to 30 m tall, bole to 6 m with short buttresses. Leaves spirally arranged, palmately compound with 5–6 entire leaflets which are elliptic-lanceolate, petioles 10–20 cm long, petiolules 1–5 mm, blades 10–15 × 2.5–7.5 cm, both surfaces with sparse stellate hairs, becoming glabrous. Inflorescences terminal or axillary panicles 11–19 cm long, with greenish-yellow flowers becoming red with a very unpleasant, foetid smell. Fruits in a cluster of 1–5 or more, reddish green, woody, curved follicles, 7.5–10 cm long × 6–9 cm wide with 1 cm acuminate spur, containing c. 20 ellipsoid, edible seeds 2–2.5 cm long, purple-black with a thin aril, rich in non-toxic oil (30%) and protein.

Distribution and Habitat: Throughout Malesia. Coastal areas both on plains and hills up to 150 m.

Vernacular Names: *kelumpang* (Malay); Java olive (English).

Notes: The seeds are eaten as nuts, often roasted, and taste like cocoa. They produce a light-yellow oil which is not toxic, with culinary use similar to olive oil, or for illumination in lamps. This species is popular with the Malays, and is cultivated as a shade tree and for famine food in India.

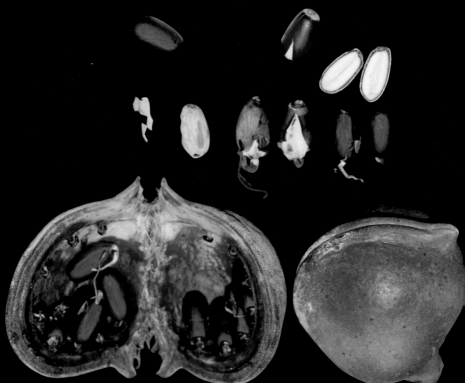

Melastoma malabathricum L.

Description: Shrub to small tree up to 3 m. Twigs covered in scales, leaves opposite or alternate up the stems, petioles 0.5–1.6 cm long, covered in scales. Blades commonly elliptic, sometimes ovate, 3–6–14 cm × 1–2–5 cm (but linear leaves in the riverine, rheophytic form of 2–5.5 cm × 1 cm), with a midvein and 2–4 longitudinal veins, the secondary veins joining the midvein at a 45° angle. Longitudinal veins and secondary veins prominent on the lower surface and covered in fine hairs, but on the upper surface, the longitudinal veins impressed and the secondary veins indistinct with very short hairs over the surface. Inflorescence a branching terminal cyme with 1, 2 or up to 10 flowers, with basal bracts. Flowers 5–6 cm diameter with pink-purple petals (white in var. *alba*), pedicels to 6 mm. Fruit a berry with persistent calyx lobes, 0.8–1.2 cm long × 0.6–0.8 cm diameter, dehiscing and exposing the orange or purple placenta with embedded seeds, which then ripens to a blackish purple. The bowl-shaped fruit is thickly covered in lanceolate, appressed scales. The small berries are sweet and tasty, but stain the lips purple.

Distribution and Habitat: Widespread from Sri Lanka, India to China, throughout Southeast Asia to the Pacific Islands. In open forest gaps or disturbed areas, from the lowlands to 1000 m, frequently found on all soil types, including ultramafics. Often found around villages, and mainly eaten by children.

Vernacular Names: *senduduk* & *kemunting* (Malay); *sekali* (Sarawak); straits rhododendron (English).

Notes: There are 41 species of *Melastoma* in Borneo of which 40 are endemic, 31 having been recently described, and many have fruits that are probably edible, but this has not been studied. This species is widespread with several forms and hybrids, and it has medicinal uses that usually result in it being cultivated in villages.

Lansium domesticum Corrêa

Description: Small to medium-sized tree, 10–30 m, bole fluted, buttress short but spreading out to 2 m. Leaves spirally arranged, pinnate leaves, petiole and rachis 30–50 cm long, petiole 5–8 cm with basal pulvinus, stipules absent, with 6–9 leaflets, alternate in a lateral plane, the terminal leaflet for cultivated forms being the largest, petiolules 5–12 mm, pubescent with basal pulvinus. Blade elliptic to oblong, 9–21 × 5–10 cm, apex shortly acuminate, base slightly asymmetric, cuneate to obtuse, upper surface glabrous, veins slightly prominent, lower surface usually pubescent with prominent veins, lateral veins 10–14 pairs. Inflorescences racemes, 4–20 cm long, solitary to 2–10 in clusters on the bole and older branches (cauliflorous and ramiflorous), with white to cream, scented, bisexual flowers, spread along the rachis. Fruits usually 15–20 developing along the rachis, ellipsoid to globose berries, 2–4 × 1.5–5 cm, with a thin epicarp to 1–1.5 mm thickness, white to pale yellow, with a sticky latex, pubescent becoming glabrous. Fruits containing 1–3 flattened, ellipsoid seeds, 13 × 7 mm, covered in a translucent white, sour to sweet aril attached to the seed. Some fruits with edible arils develop without seeds.

Distribution and Habitat: Peninsular Thailand and Malaysia, Sumatra, Java and Borneo. In lowland and hill mixed dipterocarp forest, heath forest and limestone forest to 200 m.

Vernacular Names: *langsat* (Malay); *lensat amat* (Iban), for cultivated forms, *lensat kera* (Iban) for wild forms.

Notes: The species includes distinct varieties that are widely cultivated all over Southeast Asia but are native to Peninsular Malaysia and Thailand but not in Borneo. These are referred to as *duku* or *dokong*, and the hybrid between *duku* and *langsat* is called *duku-langsat*.
This is a popular and common fruit tree, planted in villages and gardens, and commonly sold in markets. Seedless fruits are often bottled in syrup. Several select clones are available from nurseries.

Sandoricum koetjape (Burm. f.) Merr.

Description: Tree 45–50 m tall, bole 5–10 m, fluted, sometimes with buttresses up to 3 m tall. Leaves trifoliate, petiole and rachis 18–40 cm, petiole 8–16 cm long with swollen base, stipules absent, flattened on top, usually pubescent. The two basal leaflets with petiolules 4–15 mm long, with basal pulvinus, the petiolule of the apical leaflet (or it can be considered part of the rachis) 3–7 cm long. Leaflet blades ovate, glabrous above with hairs on the midrib, pubescent below, apical blade larger, 8–25 × 5–14 cm, lateral blades smaller, apex acuminate, base cuneate to obtuse, lateral leaflets with asymmetric bases, midvein and lateral veins sunken above, prominent below, with 7–14 pairs of lateral veins. Inflorescence terminal to subterminal branching panicles in the upper leaf axils of the twigs, 3–24 cm long, with basal branches to 8 cm long, the branches with fragrant, yellowish-green flowers in glomerules. Fruit a berry, roughly globose, 4–8–10 cm diameter, yellow to orange to brownish when ripe, epicarp velvety, forming a shell, pericarp to 6 mm thick, with a milky latex. Seeds 1–3, ellipsoid, with brown endocarp, 2.0–3.5 × 1.2–2 × 1–1.6 cm, forming a translucent white pulp (sarcotesta) 5–6 mm thick, which is edible, soft, juicy, and varies from sweet to very sour.

Distribution and Habitat: Peninsular Malaysia, Sumatra, Philippines, Sulawesi to New Guinea, and Borneo. Sometimes confused with the smaller fruited *S. borneense* Miq. In lowland and hill mixed dipterocarp forest up to 1200 m. Widely cultivated from selected sweet forms.

Vernacular Names: *kechapi*, *ketjapi* (Indon); *sentul* (general).

Notes: This seems to be a very variable species, and can have very heavy crops where the fruits are often smaller than normal.

Walsura pinnata Hassk.

Description: Medium-sized understorey tree, 8–12(–37) m, bole 2–11(–24) m. Leaves pinnate, petiole and rachis 12–50 cm, stipules absent, with 2–3 glabrous leaflets on each side of rachis, and one larger terminal leaflet. Petiole 9–12 cm, glabrous, flat on top, with swollen base. Leaflets with lateral petiolules to 1 cm and basal pulvinus of 5 mm, terminal petiolule to 3–5 cm, basal lateral leaflets usually smaller and elliptic to oblong to narrowly oblanceolate, 5.5–25 × 3–12 cm, terminal leaflet 15–20(–25) × 7–12 cm and apex acute to acuminate, base cuneate to obtuse for all leaflets. Lateral veins very variable in number, from 10–12 pairs to 16–20 pairs. Inflorescence a compound panicle, 9–20–35 cm long, with lower branches 3–10 cm long, terminal in leaf axils, with greenish- to yellowish-white flowers. Fruit a globose to ovoid berry, 1.2–2.5 × 1.2–2.4 cm, round in cross-section, with glabrous, thin (1 mm) epicarp, yellow to orange or reddish when ripe, pedicel 3–10 mm, with 1–2 ellipsoid seeds 1.3–2.3 × 0.9 × 1.3 cm, covered in a translucent, edible, sweet-tasting aril which is eaten fresh.

Distribution and Habitat: Indochina, Thailand, Peninsular Malaysia, Sumatra, Java, Philippines to Irian Jaya, and Borneo. In lowland to hill mixed dipterocarp forest, on a wide range of soils including ultramafic and limestone, to 900 m. Rarely cultivated.
Vernacular Names: *lantupak*, *mata kucing* (Sabah).
Notes: The fruits are eaten by hunter-gatherers. This is a variable species, and further studies are needed to see if it represents more than one species. It was previously known as *W. villamilii* Merr.

Artocarpus anisophyllus Miq.

Description: Monoecious tree to 45 m, bole to 10 m, sometimes with buttresses to 2.5 m tall, with white latex. Leaves spirally arranged, compound, pinnate, with petiole-rachis 30–100 cm, 5–10 pairs of leaflets with a terminal leaflet, and tall, pubescent stipules, 4–17 cm, enclosing the stem. Leaflets with petiolules 7 mm–4 cm long, arranged in subopposite pairs, with alternate pairs of large and small glabrous leaflets, the large leaflets reaching 20–42 × 6–12 cm, oblong or ovate-lanceolate, with asymmetric base that is cuneate, apex acuminate to 2 cm, with entire margin. Leaflets with 7–20 pairs of lateral veins, sunken above, prominent on lower surface. Inflorescence with male and female heads usually paired in the same leaf axil, male head ellipsoid-oblong, 3.0–7.5 cm long × 1.5–2 cm diameter, cream coloured when covered in pollen. Fruit compound (aggregate fruit formed by the fusion of several flowers into one head), called a syncarp, 8–10(–13) × 7–10 cm, oval or sub-globose, yellowish brown when ripe, the outer wall 6 mm thick, covered in dense rigid, cylindrical appendages (spines) 6–8 mm long, peduncle 4–6–13 cm long, syncarp containing many ellipsoid seeds, 1.7 × 1 cm, covered in an edible, sweet, orange aril. Seeds are boiled or roasted, and taste like chestnut.

Distribution and Habitat: Peninsular Malaysia, Sumatra, Bangka and Borneo. In lowland and hill mixed dipterocarp forest to 600 m. Often planted around villages, but fruits often collected from forest trees.

Vernacular Names: *mentawa* (Indon); *bintawak* (Iban); *terap ikal* (Sabah); *entawak* (general).

Notes: This is the only species in the genus which has mature pinnate leaves, which are also unique for the alternating pairs of large and small leaflets in two planes, one above the other. For tall trees in cultivation, the ripe fruits are ruined when they have fallen to the ground, which makes it difficult to harvest this species even with long bamboo poles.

Artocarpus brevipedunculatus (F.M. Jarrett) C.C. Berg

Description: Monoecious tree to 15 m tall, bole 5 m, with buttresses, white latex in all parts. Leaves simple, spirally arranged, pubescent stipules enclosing the twig 1–2.5 cm long, petioles 1.5–2.5 cm, grooved. Blade elliptic to oblanceolate, 10–30 × 6–10(–13), apex acute to acuminate, base cuneate to obtuse, upper surface glabrous, midvein and lateral veins flat, sometimes with scattered hairs, lower surface veins prominent with 6–12 pairs of lateral veins, the lower surface densely covered in rough short hairs, giving it a feeling like sandpaper. Inflorescence solitary in leaf axils, male head sub-globose, 1.5–2.5 cm diameter. Fruit compound, a syncarp, globose but often with bulging lobes, to 5 cm diameter, peduncle 1.5–3 cm long. Fruit outer wall is greenish-yellow and covered in short, cylindric, obtuse appendages c. 2 mm long with hairs. Seeds ellipsoid, 1 × 0.6 cm, covered in an edible, sweet, tasty, orange aril.

Distribution and Habitat: Endemic to Borneo (but unconfirmed for Kalimantan). In lowland and hill mixed dipterocarp forest and secondary forest, mostly as an understorey tree, up to 800 m.

Vernacular Names: *palatupai* (Iban); *temponek* (General).

Notes: Fruits in Sabah have been found having a very tasty, sweet, orange aril around the seed. This species was previously placed as a subspecies of *A. melinoxylus* Gagnep., but DNA sequencing has shown it to be a separate species, as *A. melinoxylus* is found in the Indochina region.

Artocarpus dadah Miq.

桑科　Family Moraceae

高大桂木

Description: Monoecious tree to 35 m tall, bole 2–4 m, sometimes with low buttresses, with white latex. Leaves simple, alternate, in opposite rows along the twigs, with stipules up to 5 cm, hairy, not enclosing the stem, petioles 1–3 cm. Blade obovate, obovate-oblong to elliptic oblong, 10–35 × 5–17 cm, apex acuminate, base cuneate to obtuse, margin entire. (Juvenile leaves are pinnately-lobed). Upper surface glabrous, midvein raised and lateral veins flat, all with scattered hairs, lower surface densely pubescent with prominent veins and 11–20 pairs of lateral veins. Inflorescence solitary in leaf axils, male heads globose, 0.8–1.5 cm diameter, cream, with edible pink pulp inside (see opposite). Fruit compound, a syncarp, sub-globose or obovoid (lobed), 5–7 cm diameter, peduncle 1–3 cm long, outer wall green to yellowish when ripe, smooth surface, with ellipsoid seeds, 12 × 8 mm, covered in red to pink, edible, aril and pulp, that is watery and slightly acidic.

Distribution and Habitat: Myanmar, Thailand, Peninsular Malaysia and Borneo. In lowland and hill mixed dipterocarp forest to 700 m.

Vernacular Names: *dadah* (Malay); *beruni* (Sabah); *selangking* (Iban); *tampang* (Indonesia).

Notes: *A. peltatus* Merr. is difficult to separate from this species, and is likely to be sunk, based on recent studies (pers. comm., N.J.C. Zerega) also similar to *A. glaucus* Blume, which has similar yellowish lobed fruit with yellow or cream and more acidic pulp. *A. dadah* was sunk by some authors into *A. lacucha* Buch.-Ham., but it has since been reinstated as a species. It is reported to be a deciduous tree in countries with a long dry season (e.g., Myanmar and Thailand). This species is not cultivated and is rarely sold in markets; the fruits are usually consumed by hunters and those travelling through forested areas.

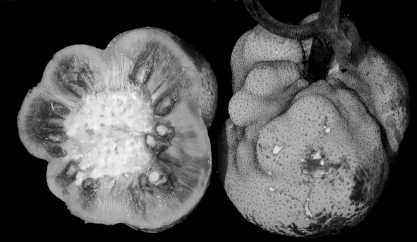

Artocarpus elasticus Reinw. ex Blume

Description: Tree, deciduous in countries with a long dry season, monoecious, to 45 m, bole to 8 m with buttresses to 3 m tall, with yellow-white latex which is often tapped for birdlime. Leaves simple, spirally arranged, with long pubescent stipules over 6 cm, enclosing the stem, petioles 4–10 cm, pubescent. Blades elliptic to oblong to ovate-elliptic, 15–60 × 10–35 cm (juvenile leaves reaching 200 cm long with 2–3 lobes), apex acute to acuminate, base cuneate to rounded, margin entire to crenate. Upper surface glabrous to sparsely hairy, midvein raised above, with flat, distinct lateral veins in 8–15 pairs, lower surface densely hairy with prominent veins. Inflorescences solitary in leaf axils, male heads 6–15 cm long × 1.5–2.5 cm diameter, cylindrical with deep grooves. Fruit, compound, a syncarp, oblong to sub-globose, 12 × 6 cm, yellow-brown when ripe, peduncle 6–12 cm, hairy. Fruit outer wall 6 mm thick, covered in closely-arranged appendages with short hairs, the longer, tapering ones to 1–1.8 cm × 1–1.5 mm and shorter conical ones 4 × 1 mm. Ellipsoid seeds, 12 × 8 mm, covered by yellowish to white edible aril that, however, often has a nauseating odour, and often tastes like rancid butter.

Distribution and Habitat: Myanmar, Peninsular Thailand and Malaysia, Sumatra, Java, and lesser Sunda Islands, Sulawesi and Borneo. In lowland and hill mixed dipterocarp forest, and secondary forest, also in lower montane forest to 1500 m.

Vernacular Names: *terap* (Malay); *talun* (Sabah); *pedali* (Iban); *tarap bulu* (Indonesian).

Notes: This species is constantly confused with *A. sericicarpus* F. M. Jarrett, which has much larger leaves and has a better fruit to eat. The bark is also used to make a cloth

and rope, and the very sticky latex is used for birdlime. The Malay name *terap* in Borneo mostly refers to *A. odoratissimus* Blanco. The seeds are often roasted and eaten like peanuts.

Artocarpus integer (Thunb.) Merr.

Description: Tree to 25 m, bole usually with no buttresses, to 1–3 m, often with bumps where cauliflorous syncarps are produced, with white latex. Leaves simple, spirally arranged, with hairy stipules 2–9 cm, enclosing the stem, petioles 1–3 cm, hairy. Blades elliptic to obovate, 5–25 cm × 2.5–12 cm, apex acuminate, base cuneate to rounded, margin entire. Upper surface glabrous, midvein and lateral veins flat, with hairs, lower surface pubescent, veins prominent, with 6–10 pairs of lateral veins. Inflorescence cauliflorous on bumps on the bole, or ramiflorous on branches, on short leafy shoots, solitary in leaf axils, male heads cylindrical to club-shaped, 3–5.5 cm × 1–1.2 cm on 3–6 cm long peduncle. Fruit, compound, a syncarp, cylindrical to globose, 20–35 cm × 10–15 cm, yellow to greenish yellow when ripe, peduncle 5–9 cm long, hairy. Fruit outer wall c. 10 mm thick, covered in closely-set, obtuse, minutely-hairy appendages of 2–4 mm × 3 mm. Seeds ellipsoid to oblong, covered in soft, fleshy yellow aril 3 × 2 cm (including seeds), which becomes detached from the core, edible, sweet, with very strong durian-like odour.

Distribution and Habitat: Sumatra, Sulawesi, Moluccas, New Guinea and Borneo. In lowland mixed dipterocarp forest to 500 m, trees in primary forest appear to have similar qualities to the cultivated ones, which are widespread in Borneo.

Vernacular Names: *cempedak* (Malay); *temedak* (Iban); *pulutan* (Sabah) *tundak* (Kalimantan); small jackfruit (English).

Notes: The young fruits are cooked as a vegetable, usually with coconut milk, to make a curry. The seeds are eaten after they are roasted, fried, or boiled. Var. *silvestris* Corner is found in Peninsular Thailand and Malaysia, Singapore and Sumatra, but with only one record from southeast Borneo—a variety with fruits that are without odour or taste. In Borneo, selected cultivars of var. *integer* are widely planted.

The similarly widely-cultivated jackfruit, *A. heterophyllus* Lam., was originally introduced from India, and also has cauliflorous fruits.

Artocarpus lanceifolius Roxb. ssp. clementis
(Merr.) Jarrett

Description: Monoecious tree to 35 m, bole to 5 m with small buttresses and white latex. Leaves simple, spirally arranged, with stipules 1–3 cm long, enclosing the stem, petioles 1–4 cm long. Blades lanceolate-elliptic to ovate-lanceolate, 12–22(–30) × 6–11(–17) cm, apex acuminate, base cuneate, margin entire. Leaves on immature trees larger with deeply lobed margins becoming entire at maturity. Upper surface glabrous with flat veins, lower surface glabrous with prominent midvein and 8–14 pairs of lateral veins. Inflorescence in leaf axils, male heads 3–6 × 1.2–1.8 cm, cylindrical. Fruit compound, a syncarp, sub-globose 8–10–12 cm × 7–8 cm, olive to brown, outer wall 8 mm thick, covered in truncate, appressed, pubescent appendages, 3.5 × 3 mm, peduncle 4–5 cm long. Seeds ellipsoid, 1.2–1.5 cm × 8 mm, covered in an edible juicy, sweet, delicious orange aril.

Distribution and Habitat: This subspecies is endemic to northeast Borneo. It is an understorey tree in lowland and hill mixed dipterocarp forest and secondary forest to 1000 m altitude. Rarely cultivated, the fruits are collected from the forest, and are sometimes sold in local markets.
Vernacular Names: *keledang* (Malay); *timakon* (Sabah); *kaliput* (Iban).
Notes: *Artocarpus lanceifolius* ssp. *lanceifolius,* which is found in Peninsular Malaysia and Sumatra, has more ovate to obovate leaves, and the aril around the seeds is white. Selected sweet varieties should be cultivated in order to develop its commercial potential.

Artocarpus limpato Miq.

Description: Tree, deciduous in countries with a long dry season, to 30 m tall, bole short, 2–4 m, sometimes with buttresses, with white latex. Leaves simple, alternately arranged in rows opposite each other on the twig, with pairs of stipules that do not enclose the stem, petioles to 3 cm, grooved. Blade 10–35 × 4–15 cm, apex long-acuminate to 2 cm, base asymmetric, cuneate to rounded, margin entire, slightly undulating. Upper surface glabrous, veins flat, lower surface glabrous with midvein and 12–14 pairs of prominent veins. Inflorescence solitary or in pairs in the leaf axils, male head globose, 1.5 cm diameter, on shorter peduncle of 3–4 cm. Fruit compound, a syncarp, irregularly globose, green with 8–20 ovoid fruits projecting out from the core, each 1.5–2 cm and c. 1 cm diameter, turning orange when ripe, peduncle 7.5–11.5 cm long. Fruits edible, the sweet orange aril often with a banana-like flavour.

Distribution and Habitat: Peninsular Malaysia, Sumatra and Borneo. In lowland to hill mixed dipterocarp forest to 700 m, often along river banks and also on limestone. Sometimes planted in rural villages.

Vernacular Names: *tampang susu* (Malay); *kesusu* (Sabah); *empatak* (Iban).

Notes: This species was originally placed in *Artocarpus*, but was later moved to another genus, *Prainea*. Recent DNA sequencing has, however, shown that it belongs in *Artocarpus*, but in the subgenus *Prainea*, because of its leaves that are not spirally arranged but alternate, and syncarp that has exposed fruits not covered by a wall or rind.

Artocarpus odoratissimus Blanco

Description: Monoecious tree to 25 m, bole 3–6 m, sometimes with low buttresses, with white latex. Leaves simple, spirally arranged, stipules 1–8 cm long, enclosing the twig, pubescent, petioles 2–3(–4) cm long, hairy, grooved on top. Blades elliptic to obovate, 16–50 × 8–28 cm, apex blunt, acute, base cuneate to obtuse, margin entire to undulate (juvenile leaves pinnately lobed), both surfaces hairy, veins prominent below, flat on upper surface with midvein slightly raised, and 9–16 pairs of lateral veins. Inflorescences both male and female in leaf axils. Male head ellipsoid to club-shaped, 4–11 × 2.5–6 cm, cream turning brown, often with folds. Fruit compound, a syncarp, sub-globose, generally 16 × 13 cm, yellowish-brown or green when ripe, peduncle 5.5–16 cm long. Fruit outer wall 5 mm thick, covered in dense, rigid, cylindrical appendages of 8–13 mm long. Seeds ellipsoid, 1.2 × 0.8 cm, covered in sweet, juicy, thick fleshy white pulp, with distinct flavour and aroma.

Distribution and Habitat: Endemic to Borneo. Introduced long ago into the southern Philippines, where it is commonly cultivated. It is also commonly cultivated all over Borneo, and has been introduced to other countries in Southeast Asia. An understorey tree in lowland and hill mixed dipterocarp forest up to 1000 m. Also in secondary forest.

Vernacular Names: *terap* (Malay); *binturong* and *marang* (Indo); *pingan* (Iban); *tarap* (Brunei & Sabah).

Notes: The seeds are boiled and roasted as a snack, and have a nutty flavour. The immature fruits are usually cooked in coconut milk and eaten as a vegetable curry, as is commonly done with jackfruit. Selected forms with larger fruits (to 3 kg) have a tastier and sweeter fleshy aril, and the best forms grow at mid-elevations at c. 500 m altitude. It now appears that the cultivated form is a triploid, and the truly wild trees with smaller fruits are now considered a subspecies (pers. comm., Elliot Gardner). *A. sarawakensis* F.M. Jarrett has similar fruits but which are less aromatic.

Artocarpus rigidus Blume ssp. rigidus

Description: Monoecious tree to 35 m, bole 3–9 m, with buttresses and white latex. Leaves simple, spirally arranged, with pubescent stipules of 0.5–3 cm enclosing the stem, petioles hairy, 1–2.5 cm long, blades elliptic to ovate to obovate, 7–20 × 5–8 cm, apex acute to acuminate, base margin entire to shallowly sinuate (juvenile leaves larger, with shallow lobes along the margin). Leaf surface glabrous above with flat veins, with some hairs along the midvein, lower surface pubescent to hairy, with prominent veins and 11–20 pairs of lateral veins. Inflorescence solitary in leaf axils, male heads 1.3–2 cm, obovoid to globose, with peduncles 2–6 mm long. Fruit compound, a syncarp, globose, 7–10 cm diameter, peduncle 2–5 cm, yellow to dull orange, the outer wall to 10 mm thick, covered in dense, stiff spine-like appendages 7–10 mm long. Seeds ellipsoid, 12 × 7 mm, covered in sweet to sub-acidic, yellow, edible aril with a citrus-like flavour.

Distribution and Habitat: Peninsular Malaysia, Sumatra, Bangka, Java and Borneo. In lowland and hill mixed dipterocarp forest to 1000 m, also in peat and fresh water swamps and limestone forest. Cultivated in Peninsular Malaysia and Java for the fruit, but sparsely planted in villages in Borneo.
Vernacular Names: *periam* or *pujun* (Malay); *pudau* (Iban); *peruput* (Sabah); *mantibungan* (Indon); monkey jackfruit (English).
Notes: *A. rigidus* has 2 subspecies. The other subspecies, ssp. *asperulus* (Gapnep.) F.M. Jarrett, occurs in Indochina and Myanmar, and has only 9–12 pairs of lateral veins, and more ovate leaves.

Artocarpus sericicarpus F.M. Jarrett

桑科　毛球波罗蜜

Family Moraceae

Description: Monoecious tree 30–40 m tall, bole to 5 m with buttresses, white latex. Leaves simple, spirally arranged, with stipules to 8 cm enclosing the twig, petioles 3–11 cm, grooved. Blade ovate to elliptic, 40–70 × 20–30 cm, apex acute to shortly acuminate, base cuneate to obtuse to rounded, margin entire to undulating. Upper surface glabrous, midvein and lateral veins flat and distinct, few hairs on veins, lower surface veins prominent with hairs, lateral veins 11–17 pairs. Inflorescence both male and female, solitary in leaf axils. Male head 10 × 2 cm, oblong. Fruit compound, a syncarp, sub-globose to ovoid, 8–15 × 5–6 cm, peduncle 3–16 cm × 4 mm, pubescent. Fruit outer wall 6 mm thick, brownish yellow when ripe, covered in dense, long, flexible, pointed appendages of 1–3 cm long × 1 mm, curved and with small hairs, and fewer shorter, conical appendages of 3–6 mm × 1 mm. Seeds ellipsoid, brown, 10 × 6 mm, covered in an edible, sweet, white aril with pleasant aroma similar to *A. odoratissimus*.

Distribution and Habitat: Philippines, Sulawesi and Borneo. In lowland to hill mixed dipterocarp forest to 1000 m. Commonly cultivated in villages.
Vernacular Names: *terap bulu* (Malay); *pedalai* (Iban); *togop* (Sabah).
Notes: This species was previously considered to be the same as *A. elasticus* Reinw., but it has much larger leaves and inflorescences, and fruits with larger appendages, and is much more preferred as an edible fruit. The seeds are boiled, fried, or roasted, and have a nutty flavour.

Artocarpus tamaran Becc.

Description: Monoecious tree to 40 m, bole to 10 m, buttresses to 3 m high, with white latex. Leaves simple, spirally arranged, stipules 3–9 cm long with reddish hairs, enclosing the twig, petioles 3–5 cm, also with reddish hairs. Blade ovate to elliptic-lanceolate, 27–35 × 10–18 cm, apex acute, base obtuse to rounded, margin entire or with lobes (juvenile leaves very distinct, up to 100 cm long with deeply pinnate lobes). Upper surface glabrous, midvein raised, lateral veins sunken, lower surface pubescent, midvein and 17–23 pairs of lateral veins prominent, creating a distinct, strongly plicate (deeply folded) leaf. Inflorescence solitary in leaf axil, male head cylindrical, 7–8 cm long × 1–1.5 cm diameter. Fruit compound, a syncarp, cylindrical to oblong, 10–15 × 5 cm, ripening yellowish, peduncle hairy 5–13 cm long. Fruit outer wall c. 8 mm thick, covered in fleshy, curved, appendages with hairs, like flexible spines, of two lengths, the longer ones up to 1 cm, and the shorter ones to 3 mm. Seeds ellipsoid, 6 × 4 mm, covered in an edible, sweet, white aril.

Distribution and Habitat: Endemic to Borneo. Common in Sabah, less common in the other states. In lowland, coastal and hill mixed dipterocarp forest to 600 m, and in secondary forest.

Vernacular Names: *tarap tempunan* (Malay); *timbangan* (Sabah); *tamaran* (Sarawak); *entawa* (Iban); *wi yang* (Indon); elephant jack (English).

Notes: This species is distinct in having plicate leaves with many pairs of lateral veins. Its edible white aril is similar in texture to *A. odoratissimus* Blanco, *A. teysmanii* Miq. and *A. sericicarpus* F. M. Jarrett but is not as good, and it also has smaller fruits. The bark of this tree was used extensively for making barkcloth by several tribes in Borneo.

Artocarpus teysmannii Miq.

Description: Monoecious tree to 45 m, bole to 7 m, with small buttresses and white latex. Leaves simple, spirally arranged, with pubescent leaf stipules to 9 cm, petioles 1–3.5(–6) cm. Blade ovate, lanceolate to obovate, 15–25(–35) × 5–10(–17) cm, apex acute, base broadly cuneate to rounded. Upper surface glabrous, veins flat, lower surface glabrous with midvein and lateral veins pubescent and prominent, 6–10(–14) pairs of lateral veins. Inflorescence solitary in leaf axils, male head 3.5–7.5 × 0.5–1 cm, cylindrical. Fruit compound, a syncarp, oblong, cylindrical, 8.5–12 × 3–6 cm, peduncle 3–10 cm, hairy. Fruit outer wall brownish yellow when ripe, 2 mm thick, covered in closely-arranged conical, hairy appendages of 4–5 mm long. Seeds ellipsoid, 7 × 6 mm, covered in sweet, white aril similar to *A. sericicarpus*.

Distribution and Habitat: Peninsular Malaysia, Sumatra, Sulawesi, Sulu Islands, to western New Guinea and Borneo. Rare in Sabah, more common in Sarawak and East Kalimantan. In lowland to hill mixed dipterocarp forest and swamp forest to 1000 m.

Vernacular Names: *cempedak air* (Malay); *tilap* (Indon).

Notes: This appears to be a rare species in the wild, with similar tasting fruits to *A. tamaran* Becc. and *A. sericicarpus* F.M. Jarrett. It is not known to be cultivated.

桑科

船木波罗蜜

Ficus callosa Willd.

Description: Tall tree to 45 m with a smooth white bole to 20 m, large buttresses, and exuding white latex if cut. Juvenile plants have large lobed leaves. Mature trees are deciduous with a short flush of new leaves, and have glabrous, spirally arranged leaves with petioles 3–7(–11) cm which are grooved, with stipules 1–3 cm long. Blades elliptic to oblong to obovate, 12–20(–35) × 5–15(–20) cm, apex blunt to acute, base rounded, midvein prominent on both surfaces, with 9–12 pairs of lateral veins, those on the upper surface indistinct. Inflorescence monoecious, with figs solitary or in pairs on long stalks (peduncle + pedicel), from axils of the leaves at the ends of twigs (making them accessible to bats which feed on them and disperse the seeds). Figs with pedicels 0.5–2 cm long, 3 basal bracts, the syconia globose to ovoid, 2–5 × 1.5–4.5 cm diameter, ripening yellowish green, edible if cooked. Seeds small and hard, and are bat-dispersed.

Distribution and Habitat: India, Sri Lanka, Thailand, Myanmar, Indochina, north Peninsular Malaysia, south Sumatra, Java, Moluccas, the Philippines, northeast Sulawesi and north Borneo. In Borneo, it is only in Sabah, and is found in lowland secondary forest and in urban areas, and also in lowland mixed dipterocarp forest, especially in river valleys.

Vernacular Names: *tempanara* (Malay) (Iban).

Notes: The fig is a specialised reproductive body called a syconia, formed by the receptacle of the flower surrounding the flowers to form a compound inflorescence and later the fruit. An ostiole (narrow entrance) at the apex of the syconia gives access to fig wasps that pollinate the flowers and also breed inside in special gall flowers.

Ficus nota (Blanco) Merr.

Description: Small tree to 13 m tall, bole 3–5 m, with white latex. Leaves spirally arranged, petioles 1–6(–8) cm long, stipules 1–3 cm. Blade asymmetric, 15–35 cm long × 7.5–21 cm wide, elliptic to oblong, apex acuminate, base cordate to sub-ovate on one side, and cordate to rounded on the wider side, margins crenate to dentate, midvein and 4–9 pairs of lateral veins depressed and distinct on upper surface, which is sparsely pubescent becoming glabrous, prominent on lower surface, with a dense covering of short, soft hairs. Inflorescence dioecious, cauliflorous on the bole and main branches, with clusters of figs on leafless branches up to 60 cm long. Peduncles of figs 0.5–2.5(–5) cm long. Figs pyriform to obovoid, 2.5–4.5 cm diameter with 3 basal bracts, with 1 or 2 lateral bracts, and a finely-ribbed, glabrous surface with distinct lenticels, ripening greenish-yellow to brown, ostiole 4–6 mm. Figs edible, sweetish, eaten fresh.

Distribution and Habitat: Philippines and Borneo (Sabah only). Lowland mixed dipterocarp forest and hill forest, to lower montane forest at 1300 m, often along streams.

Vernacular Names: *ara hutan* (Malay).

Notes: This species is sometimes established in villages in hill forest. The male fig trees attract many ants to feed on emerging fig wasps, and the figs are not eaten; only the figs from female trees are consumed.

Ficus racemosa L.

Description: Medium-sized tree to 30 m high, whitish bole to 2 m, with buttresses and white latex. Wide-spreading white branches. Leaves spirally arranged, petioles 1.5–7 cm with stipules to 1.2–2 cm, blade oblong to lanceolate to sub-ovate, symmetric, 6–20 cm long × 3–9 cm wide, apex acute to acuminate, base cuneate to rounded with entire margin. Upper surface glossy, dark green, sparsely hairy becoming glabrous, midvein appressed, with 4–9–12 pairs of faintly distinct lateral veins, lower surface with prominent veins, surface sparsely hairy to glabrous. Inflorescence monoecious, cauliflorous, on the bole and main branches. Figs in clusters up to 25 cm long on leafless branches, mostly pendulous. Syconia with peduncle 0.3–1.2 cm long, with 3 basal bracts, sub-globose, 3–5 cm diameter, without lateral bracts, apical ostiole of 3 mm diameter. Figs ripen from green to yellow, orange and pink or red. Edible, sweetish to bland tasting, eaten by many animals and fish.

Distribution and Habitat: Sri Lanka, India to south China, Malesia region except Philippines, to northern Australia, and Borneo. Lowland forests, mainly along rivers, and also in secondary forest areas.

Vernacular Names: *ara lempong* or *tangkol* (Malay); *nunuk ragang* (Sabah); red river fig or cluster fig (English).

Notes: This species is an important food source for many animals, especially during non-fruiting season. It is a famine food eaten by people travelling or living along rivers. The *Nunuk Ragang* is of great cultural significance to the Kadazan-Dusun people of Sabah, who celebrate an annual *nunuk ragang* festival at Tampias, and revere this 'Garden of Eden', which represents the origin of all their tribes. This species has frequently been confused with a similar species, *F. obpyramidata* King, but that only occurs in Peninsular Malaysia, Thailand, to Myanmar.

Ficus uncinata (King) Becc.

Description: Shrub or small tree to 8 m, often with a clear bole up to 1–2 m, from which specialised flowering branches called stolons occur at the base or above ground level, and run along the ground for several metres, often branching. Leaves drooping, petioles 1.5–2 cm, greenish-brown, hirsute, with 1.5 cm long, hairy stipules. Blades lanceolate to sub-ovate, 21–25(–27) × 10–11 cm, asymmetric, the base on the narrow side cuneate to subcordate, and rounded on the broader side, the apex acute to acuminate, margins dentate along lower half to serrate in upper half, midvein flat on pubescent upper surface, prominent, 8–12(–14) pairs of lateral veins prominent on the sub-hirsute lower surface. Inflorescence flagelliferous, arranged along stolons to 10 m long, figs (syconia) sessile or with 6 mm peduncle, with 3 basal bracts, globose to pyriform, 2–4 cm diameter, pink to red to brownish purple, with several incurved lateral bracts, the ostiole 4–5 mm in diameter with rosette of small apical bracts. Figs edible if female with seeds.

Distribution and Habitat: Borneo, and not certain for Sumatra. Widespread, common along streams, especially in wetter zones, and more common in hill areas to montane forest up to 2000 m.

Vernacular Names: *ara entimau* (Iban); earth fig (English).

Notes: The species is very variable and has been confused with at least 4 other species, namely, *Ficus beccarii* King, *F. geocharis* Corner, *F. megaleia* Corner and *F. subterranea* Corner. Borneo has eight species of earth figs, of which six are endemic and several are edible.

Musa lawitiensis Nasution & Supard. var. suratii

Description: Perennial herb, the stem a corm, producing roots and an erect-leafy shoot or pseudo stem from a growing point on top of the corm, followed by suckers from the side of the corm, thereby forming a cluster of up to 7 pseudo stems to 3.5 m tall. Base of pseudo stem covered in spirally arranged, green to reddish-purple leaf sheaths, above which are the leaves, petioles c. 25 cm long, the base of 10 cm long clasping the stem. Blade elliptic, 140 × 20 cm, apex long acuminate, base asymmetric, obtuse, margin entire, upper and lower surfaces glabrous, midvein prominent and yellowish-green above, orange below, with many densely-packed, corrugate lateral veins, the lower surface white, waxy. Inflorescence single, from the apex of the pseudo stem, hanging downwards, peduncle reddish, 20 cm long × 3.5 cm diameter, the rachis with a basal, reddish sterile bract which falls off as the female flowers open, the female bud covered in reddish bracts that also fall off, revealing a cluster or 'hand' of cream, 9 cm long, hermaphrodite flowers, in 2 rows. Male bud apical, pointed, 14 × 2.2 cm, with 4–6 yellowish male flowers in a single row per bract, falling off together. The final bunch of fruits comprises 4–10 separate hands of fruits, each hand made up of 2 rows of 5–8 finger-like, erect fruits, each to 10 cm long, pedicels 6 mm long, fruits curved and round in cross-section, the 'peel' turning yellow when ripe, containing yellow, soft creamy pulp with up to 100 seeds of 1 mm diameter.

Distribution and Habitat: Endemic to Borneo. Found in hill mixed dipterocarp forest, 150–1000 m, usually on slopes of ridges.
Vernacular Names: *kenjuai* (Iban).
Notes: This is one of 14 native *Musa* species found in Borneo. There are many species that have fruits with edible pulp and are full of seeds but are not eaten, unlike the delicious, edible *M. acuminata* × *balbisiana* cultivars that cultivated all over Borneo. *M. lawitiensis* consists of a total of 4 named varieties: var. *lawitiensis*, var. *suratii*, var. *kapitensis* and var. *sarawakensis* that are cultivated. The Iban of Sarawak eat the immature fresh fruit in a salad (*ulam*).

Rhodomyrtus tomentosa (Aiton) Hassk.

Description: Bushy shrub to 4 m, evergreen but with short leaf flushes at least annually. Leaves opposite, petioles 3–7 mm long, grooved above. Blade elliptic to lanceolate to oblong, base and apex obtuse, 4–10 × 2.3–4 cm, dark green and glabrous above, pale whitish-green and woolly below, 3 distinct longitudinal veins, with the outer ones near to the entire leaf margins, secondary veins indistinct on the upper surface but distinct on the lower surface, perpendicular to the midvein and joining the outer veins. Inflorescence with solitary flowers or a cyme of 3 flowers, in leaf axils, flowers to 4 cm diameter, petals magenta or pink fading to white, with green ovary, calyx lobes and flower stalk 1–2 cm, with two basal green bracts. Fruit a berry, oblong to ovoid, 10–15 × 8–12 mm, green turning red to purple when ripe, pedicel to 1 cm, crowned by calyx lobes, epicarp thin with woolly surface, mesocarp (pulp) red to purple, edible, juicy, sweet, with many small seeds to 1.5 × 1 mm.

Distribution and Habitat: Southeast Asia, India to China, and south to Australia. Found in open areas on sandy soils, especially along coastal areas and sandy ridge tops up to 300 m, but rarely up to 1300 m. Selected forms are cultivated. Another wild variety, *parviflora,* is found in Sri Lanka and India.
Vernacular Names: *kemunting* (Malay); rose myrtle (English).
Notes: The native variety, *tomentosa*, is often found around coastal villages in open areas, and because the fruit is popular with children, it is often spread to villages and cultivated areas in the interior regions too. As the plants and their flowers are similar to those of *Melastoma malabathricum*, and the fruits of both species are mainly eaten by children, they may both be referred to '*kemunting*'. However, fruits of cultivated varieties are far superior to the wild ones.

Family Myrtaceae

桃金娘科

桃金娘

Scorodocarpus borneensis (Baill.) Becc.

Description: Medium to large tree to 40 m, with a small crown, bole to 25 m, older trees with small buttresses, bark and all parts of the tree with a smell of garlic. Leaves simple, alternately arranged in a lateral plane, glabrous, upper surface shiny dark green, petioles 1.5–2.5 cm with a distal pulvinus, no stipules. Blade elliptic, 10–25 × 4–9 cm, apex acuminate, base rounded to wedge shaped, margin entire, with 5–6 pairs of lateral veins. Inflorescences to 4 cm in leaf axils, with 2–3 white, bisexual flowers in clusters. Fruit a drupe, green, globose, to 3–5 cm diameter, pedicel 1 cm long. Epicarp thin and fleshy, seeds sub-globose, with a thin, woody endocarp, and white endosperm which is edible.

Distribution and Habitat: Peninsular Thailand and Peninsular Malaysia, Sumatra and Borneo. Found in alluvial flood plains in lowland dipterocarp forest, and hill forest slopes on clay soils, up to 150 m (rarely to 500 m).

Vernacular Names: *bawang hutan* or *kulim* (Malay); *sindik* or *sindu* (Iban); onion tree or garlic-nut tree (English).

Notes: This is a monotypic genus with a single species that is common and widespread in lowland forests. It is seldom cultivated as it is slow growing, and is mainly grown for its timber (called *kulim*). The fruits are usually collected from the forest. They are boiled, and the kernel eaten by many tribes throughout Borneo, while the leaves are used for flavouring in cooking.

Sarcotheca diversifolia (Miq.) Hallier f.

Description: Small to medium-sized tree to 30 m, the bole to 5 m, fluted, sometimes with buttresses to 2 m. Leaves spirally arranged, trifoliate, glabrous, the terminal leaflet twice the size of the lateral ones, petiole-rachis 1–3.5 cm with distal pulvinus, stipules absent, lateral leaflets ovate to elliptic, petiolules 5–10 mm, blade 3–6(–10) × 1–2(–5) cm, apex acuminate, base rounded, terminal leaflet 13–20 × 4–6 cm, apex acuminate, base obtuse to rounded. Each leaflet with 2–5 pairs of lateral veins. Inflorescence a cluster of 1–4 panicles, to 13 cm long, from leaf axils, branching, with pink and purple bisexual flowers. Fruit a berry, 1.5 × 1 cm to 3 × 2 cm, ellipsoid, glabrous, green to yellowish-green or yellow when ripe, with a thin epicarp, and fleshy, juicy mesocarp, translucent to white, with none to seven seeds, each 6–7 × 4–5 mm, with smooth testa. Edible sweet to sour pulp, eaten raw or cooked with meat or vegetables.

Distribution and Habitat: Sumatra and Borneo. In mixed lowland to hill dipterocarp forest, secondary forest, and mixed swamp and peat forest to 900 m.

Vernacular Names: *pupoi* or *belimbing bulat* (Malay); *tabarus* (Sabah, Brunei); *piang* (Sarawak); *belimbing hutan* (Indonesia).

Notes: This species is not very common, but is cultivated in some villages. The ripe fruits look like a rounder *bilimbi* (*Averrhoa bilimbi* L, a species in a related genus).

Baccaurea angulata Merr.

Description: Small to medium dioecious tree 6–21 m, bole c. 2–3–5 m, normally with no buttresses. Leaves simple, spirally arranged in clusters, stipules 4–11 mm, not enclosing the stem, petioles 2–12 cm long, glabrous, with basal pulvinus. Blade lanceolate to elliptic to obovate, 12–39 × 4–14 cm, apex acuminate, sometimes obtuse, base cuneate to sometimes obtuse to rounded, lower surface glabrous, glands absent, veins raised, upper surface glabrous, midvein slightly raised, lateral veins distinctly impressed, 9–12(–16) pairs. Male inflorescences with minute branches, to 23 cm long, several clustered along branches and on the bole, with up to 50 yellow flowers scattered along the rachis, female inflorescences to 25 cm long, in clusters, up to 7 per cluster, with pale yellow to cream flowers on bole and branches. Fruit a berry, obovoid, immature fruits dark purple ripening bright red, 5.0–6.0 × 2.3–2.6 cm, pedicel 4–8 mm long. Fruit star-shaped in cross section, with distinct ridges on the outer surface of the epicarp which is c. 2 mm thick, and 2–3 ellipsoid, laterally-flattened seeds, 1.6–2.3 × 0.7–1.6 × 0.4 × 0.9 cm covered in an edible, sweet to sour, white arillode.

Distribution and Habitat: Endemic to Borneo. In lowland and hill mixed dipterocarp forest, riverine and secondary forest to 800 m. Often cultivated in villages, fruits are also collected from forest trees and sold in markets.

Vernacular Names: *belimbing hutan* or *belimbing darah* (Malay); *ucong* (Iban); *embaling* (Sabah).

Notes: This is a very distinct species compared to other round fruited, *Baccaurea* or *tampoi* species, with its angled fruits, and long leaves. Like other species of *tampoi* in cultivation, male trees must be planted to allow pollination, otherwise fruits produced will have no seeds with an arillode for eating. Another problem is that <90% of seeds planted grow into male trees. The red, angular epicarp of this species is pickled with salt, or a preserve is made with sugar, and the pulp also produces a delicious juice.

Baccaurea lanceolata (Miq.) Müll. Arg.

Description: Dioecious tree to 30 m, bole variable, 1–3 m, very gnarled where cauliflorous inflorescences emerge, no buttresses formed. Leaves simple, spirally arranged in clusters, stipules to 1.6 cm, petioles 1.6–18 cm long, with normally both proximal and distal (apical) pulvina. Blade ovate to elliptic to obovate, 9–35 × 3.0–15 cm, apex acute, base obtuse to rounded, upper surface glabrous, midvein slightly raised, lateral veins impressed, lower surface glabrous, glands present, veins prominent, with 6–13 pairs of lateral veins. Inflorescences cauliflorous, usually in clusters, male inflorescences 4–18 cm long, with many yellow to cream to pink flowers scattered along the rachis on minute branches. Female inflorescence 8–40 cm long with 20–25 yellow to reddish cream to purple flowers. Fruits berries, globose to ellipsoid, 6 × 4 cm, usually green or beige, ripening yellow to orange, with pedicels 3–17 mm. Epicarp 1 mm thick, mesocarp around 1–4 laterally-flattened, ellipsoid seeds, 1.2–2.6 × 0.8–1.5 × 0.5–0.9 cm, covered in a white to translucent arillode, and with the white mesocarp, are sour to acid.

Distribution and Habitat: Thailand, Peninsular Malaysia, Sumatra, north Java, Philippines (Palawan) and Borneo. Mostly in lowland and hill mixed dipterocarp forest, and flood plains or secondary forest, also occurring in upper hill forest and lower montane forest to 1300 m. Seldom seen in cultivation.

Vernacular Names: *rambai hutan* (Malay); *empaung* or *lampong* (Iban); *limpasu* (Sabah, general).

Notes: The sour mesocarp and arillode are often cooked or eaten as *ulam* with salt, sugar, or prawn paste, or they are made into pickles. It is also sometimes cooked with chicken rice, but mostly with fish. This species mostly fruits all year round, and although it is sometimes cultivated in villages, the fruits are mostly collected from the forest. When in cultivation without male trees, and far from the forest, trees may produce fruits with no seeds but which are full of mesocarp and can still be utilised.

Baccaurea macrocarpa (Miq.) Müll. Arg.

Description: Small to medium-sized dioecious tree, 5–27 m, bole to 6 m, fluted up to 5 m, sometimes with small buttresses. Leaves simple, alternate to spirally arranged in clusters, stipules to 9 cm, petioles 2–14 cm long, grooved, glabrous to sparsely hairy, with distal and proximal pulvina. Blade ovate to elliptic to obovate, 9–22(–37) × 4–8(–17) cm, apex obtuse to acuminate, base cuneate to obtuse, upper surface glabrous, veins impressed, lower surface glabrous, with prominent veins that are sparsely hairy, and 6–8(–10) pairs of secondary veins, glands often present. Inflorescence mostly ramiflorous on branches, but also cauliflorous on the upper bole, in clusters. Male inflorescences to 13 cm long, usually with hairy rachis, branching, with many yellow to white flowers. Female inflorescences up to 3 in a cluster, 4–18 cm long, rachis hairy, with up to 8 fruits developing. Fruits globose, fleshy capsules, 3–6.5 × 3–7.5 × 3–7.5–8 cm, with dehiscent locules, with 3–6 seeds, pedicels 0.7–3 cm long. Epicarp and mesocarp to 11 mm thick, glabrous with glands (dark spots), ripening yellowish-brown to reddish-brown. Seeds ellipsoid to globose, 1.3–2.3 × 1.1–2.3 × 0.4–0.7 cm, flattened, covered in a translucent white or yellowish arillode, edible, juicy, sweet, soft, with a fruity fragrance.

Distribution and Habitat: Peninsular Malaysia, Sumatra, Ambon and Borneo. In lowland and hill mixed dipterocarp forest, swampy forest, and sometimes in secondary forest. More common in lowland forest, but occurs in lower montane forest up to 1600 m.

Vernacular Names: *tampoi* or *tampoi putih* (Malay); *puak* (Iban); *tampoi batang* (general); *kapul* (Indon); greater tampoi (English).

Notes: This is probably the most common of the many edible *tampoi* with globose 'capsular-like' fruits that are ramiflorous on the branches to sometimes cauliflorous on the upper bole, and which have a dehiscent fruit wall, and a sweet to sour arillode. This is a popular fruit, and is commonly cultivated, and sold in markets. In Sarawak, the fruits are also used to make a fruit wine.

Baccaurea motleyana (Müll. Arg.) Müll. Arg.

Description: Understorey small to medium dioecious tree, 8–20(–27) m with short bole 1–2 m, sometimes fluted with small buttresses. Leaves simple, spirally arranged, stipules to 1 cm, petioles 2–8 cm, pubescent, with proximal pulvinus. Blade elliptic to obovate, 13–37 × 5–15 cm, apex acute to cuspidate, base rounded, margin undulating with marginal glands present, upper surface glabrous, veins impressed, lower surface pubescent, with prominent hairy veins, glands absent, with 10–17 pairs of lateral veins. Male inflorescences in axils of leaves, solitary and up to 5 cm, or in a cluster, 3–24 cm long, with greenish-yellow flowers scattered along the rachis. Female inflorescences ramiflorous along branches to cauliflorous on bole, either solitary or in clusters of 5, 13–42 cm long, with green to yellow flowers, pendulous with fruits. Fruit globose to ellipsoid, with 0.5–1 cm pedicel, a 3-seeded berry, 2–4.5 × 1.5–2.5 × 2.5 cm, with a glabrous to pubescent, yellow epicarp when ripe, the epicarp and mesocarp to 1.5 mm thick. Seeds ellipsoid, laterally-flattened, 1.3–2 × 0.9–1.4 × 0.3–0.4 cm covered in translucent white arillode that is edible and sour to sweet.

Distribution and Habitat: Peninsular Malaysia, Sumatra and Borneo. In lowland to hill mixed dipterocarp forest, riverine forest, and secondary forest to 500 m. Commonly cultivated in villages and urban areas, and the fruits sold in markets.

Vernacular Names: *rambai* (Malay); *pekan* (Iban).

Notes: This is quite a spectacular tree when in full fruit, with hundreds of pendulous infructescences on the branches and bole. Sour fruits are used to make a vinegar.

Family Phyllanthaceae

叶下珠科

多脉木奶果

Baccaurea odoratissima Elmer

Description: Treelet to small dioecious tree, 2–17 m, bole to 4 m on taller trees, no buttresses. Leaves simple, spirally arranged, stipules to 8 mm, petioles 1–8 cm, hairy, with distal and proximal pulvinus. Blade elliptic to ovate to obovate, 6–19 × 2–10 cm, apex acute to cuspidate, base cuneate to attenuate, surfaces glabrous, midvein and lateral veins slightly hairy and prominent on lower surface, with 3–8 pairs of lateral veins. Male inflorescences in axils of leaves or ramiflorous, solitary to a few in a cluster 1.5–8 cm long, with pale yellow flowers scattered along the raceme. Female racemes solitary or in clusters of 3 or more, 2–26 cm long, cauliflorous on most of the bole, also some ramiflorous, with fruits developing along the whole raceme. Fruits globose to sub-globose fleshy capsules, 0.7–1.2 × 8–1.3 × 6–1.1 cm, splitting irregularly, with 1–2 seeds, pedicels 3–10 mm long. Epicarp and mesocarp thin, 0.5 mm, glabrous, red outside, inner surface white, with ellipsoid seeds, 6.5–10 × 3–8 × 2.5–6 mm, laterally-flattened, covered in a blue arillode which is edible and sweet to sour.

Distribution and Habitat: Endemic to Borneo. In mixed lowland and hill dipterocarp forest to 1200 m on sandstone soils, but also reported from basalt soils. Also in secondary forest, but rarely cultivated.

Vernacular Names: *kunau kunau* (Malay); *enkuni* (Iban); *kunau* (Brunei).

Notes: *B. trunciflora* Merr. described later in the 1960s with distinct red cauliflorous fruits, is now considered the same species. The blue aril tends to give the impression that it is not edible.

Baccaurea polyneura Hook. f.

Description: Medium-sized dioecious tree, 11–30 m, bole to 3–6 m, fluted or with small buttresses at the base. Leaves simple, spirally arranged, usually grouped at the ends of the twigs, stipules up to 1 cm, petioles 3–5–7 cm, finely pubescent (velvety), with distal and proximal pulvina. Blade ovate to elliptic, 10–15–20(–25) × 4–8–12(–16) cm, apex acute, base rounded, upper surface glabrous with hairs on the veins, lower surface pubescemt with prominent midvein and lateral veins, with 7–14 (commonly 8–10) pairs of lateral veins, with glands sometimes present. Inflorescences arranged with male racemes either solitary or up to 5 clustered in leaf axils or just below the leaves, 2–7 cm long, with greenish-yellow flowers clustered near the apex. Female inflorescences arranged in lower leaf axils but mostly ramiflorous along the branches, solitary or in clusters up to 3, usually 3–35 cm long with up to 50 yellow flowers. Fruits globose to sub-globose, 1–3 seeded capsules, 1–2.6 × 1.2–2.6 × 1.2–2.6 cm, with a pedicel 0.5–1.5 cm. Epicarp and mesocarp to 4 mm thick, ripening yellow to orange, surface velvety, the locules splitting open to reveal the orange arillode to 4 mm thick around laterally-flattened, ellipsoid seeds, 8–10 × 3–4 mm. The arillode is juicy, often sweet with a good flavour.

Distribution and Habitat: South Thailand, Peninsular Malaysia, Sumatra and Borneo. In lowland and hill mixed dipterocarp forest, swamp forest, and secondary forest to 800 m. Sometimes cultivated, and a popular fruit, eaten in villages near to forest.

Vernacular Names: *rambai kuning* (general); *jentik-jentik* (Malay); *jelintik* (Iban).

Notes: This species was previously referred to as *B. hookeri* Gage, and also cannot be clearly separated from *B. kunstleri* King ex Gage.

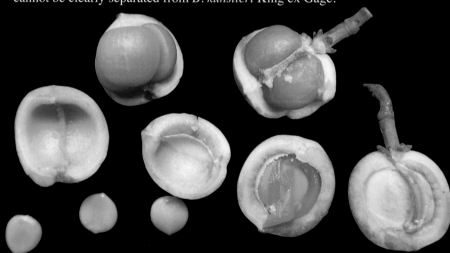

Baccaurea tetrandra (Baill.) Müll. Arg.

Description: Understorey treelet to dioecious small tree, 4–10(–20) m, commonly 6–10 m, short bole 1–1.5 m, sometimes fluted, no buttresses. Branches laterally held in whorls (like *Terminalia* species). Leaves simple, spirally arranged in clusters, stipules to 1 cm, petioles glabrous, 0.5–3–7 cm with proximal pulvinus, but often varying from 3–6 cm long in the same cluster of 3–6 leaves. Blades obovate to elliptic, 5–21 × 2–12 cm, apex obtuse to acute, base cuneate to rounded, margin entire to undulate. Upper surface glabrous, veins slightly raised, lower surface glabrous, veins prominent with 4–9 pairs of lateral veins, marginal glands present. Male inflorescences in axils of leaves, either single or 2–3 in a cluster 2–17 cm long, flowers scattered along rachis, usually white but sometimes red. Female inflorescences in lower leaf axils or below leaves, and ramiflorous on branches, single or up 3 in a cluster, 3–30 cm long, with up to 50 green to yellow or sometimes red flowers, becoming pendulous with over 20 fruits. Fruits globose to ellipsoid, capsular berries, 0.7–1.3(–1.7) × 0.5–0.9(–1.5) × 1–1.5 cm, slightly laterally-flattened, with 1–4 fleshy capsules, 1–4 seeds, and pedicels 5–8 mm long. Epicarp and mesocarp to 1–1.5 mm thick, glabrous, usually pink to red. Locules dehisce, splitting open to reveal obovoid, laterally-flattened seeds, 7–13 × 5–9 × 3–7 mm, covered in an edible, sweet to sour, blue to purple arillode.

Distribution and Habitat: Borneo, Philippines, Sulawesi and Moluccas. In lowland and hill mixed dipterocarp forest, secondary forest and swamp forest, also to 1500 m in lower montane forest, and sometimes cultivated in villages.

Vernacular Names: *mata kunau* (Malay); *kunau-kunau* (Sabah & Sarawak); *enkuni* (Kal); *kunau* (Brunei).

Notes: *Baccaurea stipulata* J. J. Sm. is a species with larger leaves, but the fruits are so similar that it cannot be separated from *B. tetrandra*, and has now been included in this species.

Xanthophyllum stipitatum A.W. Benn.

Description: Mid canopy tree to 50 m tall, bole to 9 m, sometimes with buttresses to 2 m tall. Leaves simple, alternate in a lateral plane, without stipules (but axillary buds can be confused for them), petioles 3–10 mm, glabrous. Blade glabrous, ovate to elliptic, 3–4–14 × 2–7 cm, apex acute to acuminate, base cuneate to rounded, margin entire. Upper surface with midvein and lateral veins impressed (sunken), prominent below, with 5–7 pairs of lateral veins, and glands near the base and centre of the blade. Inflorescence a raceme with 6–14 white flowers, often near the apex of the twig or in leaf axils. Fruits, berry-like, indehiscent, with 4–12 seeds, globose, 3–6 cm diameter, pedicel 1–1.5 cm long, the epicarp and mesocarp forming a shell 5–15 mm thick, smooth and glabrous outside, turning from green to yellow or orange when ripe, containing several ellipsoid brown seeds over 1 cm long, covered in a mucilaginous, edible white pulp (sarcotesta) attached to the seed coat, which is sweet to sweet-sour.

Distribution and Habitat: Widely distributed but known as native in Peninsular Malaysia, Sumatra and Borneo. In lowland and hill dipterocarp forest, also recorded from lower montane forest, peatswamp, heath forest and forest on ultramafic soils. Not commonly cultivated.

Vernacular Names: *langgir* (Malay); *nyalin paya* (Iban); *rangil* (Sabah).

Notes: *Xanthophyllum stipitatum* was previously separated from *X. amoenum* Chodat based on its consistently smaller leaves and size of the petals, but after examining many more collections, they are currently considered the same in a broader species concept. Other species reported to have edible fruits are *X. affine* Korth. ex Miq., *X. obscurum* A.W. Benn. and *X. rufum* A.W. Benn. The fruits of this species are usually collected from the forest, and are sold in village markets. The epicarp (shell) is dried and used for making shampoo.

Heliciopsis artocarpoides (Elmer) Sleumer

Description: Small tree 5–15 m, often with a crooked trunk, with low branches. Leaves simple, spirally arranged, lobed, petioles 8–16 cm, thickened at the base, stipules absent. Blade glabrous, 40–90 × 30–40 cm, with 4–6 lobes on either side of the midvein, lobes 15–30 × 3–10 cm, oblong to lanceolate with blunt apex, with 10–15 pairs of lateral veins. Inflorescences cauliflorous with some ramiflorous, either single to 3 racemes, 15–30 cm long, with dense white to yellowish fragrant flowers. Fruits drupes, cylindrical to ellipsoid, 3–4 cm long, 2–3 cm diameter. Immature fruits purple, turning green to yellow when ripe. Epicarp, thin, shiny and smooth, mesocarp soft with radial brown fibres, edible, sweet. Seeds enclosed by a brown woody endocarp.

Distribution and Habitat: Borneo and Philippines (Palawan & Mindanao). Lowland dipterocarp forest to mixed hill forest, also recorded in lower montane forest up to 1600 m.
Vernacular Names: *kurunggu* or *putat* (Malay).
Notes: It does not appear to be cultivated, and is purely a forest fruit eaten by hunter-gatherers and villagers collecting edible fruits from the forest.

Rubus fraxinifolius Poir.

Description: Erect, cane-like shrub, 2–3 m tall, with thorns or prickles to 6 mm on the stems. Leaves pinnate, with up to 4 pairs of opposite leaflets, and a terminal leaflet, petiole-rachis to 27 cm long, petioles 2–6 cm long, with linear stipules to 1.3 cm long at the base. Leaflets elliptic, lanceolate to oblong, 2–9 × 1.4 cm, apex acuminate to long pointed, base obtuse to cordate, with distinct serrate margins, petiolules c. 5 mm. Both surfaces sparsely hairy, especially on veins, with 7–10(–15) pairs of lateral veins. Inflorescences panicles, 6 to 20 cm long with up to 7 branches, sometimes with prickles, and many white, bisexual flowers with distinct calyx lobes. Fruits small drupes, massed together on a central stalk (called a collective fruit), orange to red, ovoid, up to 2.5 × 1.5 cm, with basal calyx lobes, on pedicels of 1–2 cm long. Each drupe with a single tiny seed 1.5 × 0.8 mm, with thin, red to orange epicarp and mesocarp, sweet to acidic and not very juicy, often referred to as tasteless, but this varies with location.

Distribution and Habitat: Taiwan, Philippines, Borneo (Kalimantan, Sabah and Sarawak), Sulawesi, Java, New Guinea, Solomon Islands. In open areas, river banks, areas eroded by landslides, roadsides, in lowland to montane forest to 3000 m.

Vernacular Names: *ragimot* (Sabah); mountain raspberry (English).

Notes: It is often eaten by mountain climbers, though it has been reported to be rather tasteless. Members of the Rubus subgenus *Ideobatus*, such as this species, have pinnate leaves and tall canes which are typical of raspberries. Fruits in other countries such as Java are sold in markets, and made into jams.

Family Rosaceae

薔薇科

兰屿桤叶悬钩子

226

Rubus moluccanus L.

Description: Scrambling or climbing shrub, with thorny stems 6–10 m long. Leaves simple, very variable, broadly ovate to cordate, variously lobed, petioles with thorns, 2–6 cm long, stipules to 1.7 cm, soon falling off. Blades 6–20 × 4–15 cm, variable, either with 3–5(–7) lobes and 5–9 pairs of lateral veins, or palmate with 7 main veins, apex acute to acuminate, base cordate, margins serrate, upper surface hairy, lower surface densely hairy. Inflorescence terminal to subterminal, compound raceme or panicle 20–30 cm long, with up to 12 branches, each to 5 cm with up to 30 bisexual, white to pink flowers. Fruits consist of many small drupes on a stalk (called a collective fruit, and often referred to as a berry), globular in shape, to 1 cm diameter. Individual drupes 2–3 × 1–2 mm with a single tiny seed, with thin, red epicarp and red, edible, fleshy mesocarp. The plant and fruits look like the temperate bramble or blackberry, except that the fruit is red, sweet, but with little taste.

Distribution and Habitat: From Thailand, Vietnam, through Malesia to Australia and Fiji. Lowland to montane habitats to 2000 m in open areas, river banks, areas eroded by landslides, and secondary forest.

Vernacular Names: *akar duri berumbet* (Malay); *emperingat* (Iban); tropical blackberry or bramble (English).

Notes: The fruits are sometimes made into jams. It is not cultivated, but can often be seen in cleared areas and along roadsides. Three varieties out of four for this species have been recorded for Borneo based on their leaf shapes. This species belongs to the subgenus *Malachobatus* that has simple leaves compared to compound pinnate leaves.

Family Rosaceae

薔薇科

马六甲悬钩子

Morinda citrifolia L.

Description: Tall shrub or small tree to 9 m, short bole 1–2 m, no buttresses. Leaves simple, opposite in two alternate rows, pinnately veined, stipules in pairs in leaf axils (not amplexicaule), petioles 1–1.5 cm long. Blade glabrous, broadly elliptic to obovate, 17–25(–30) × 10–13(–15) cm, apex acute, base cuneate to obtuse to rounded, margin entire (in juvenile trees, petioles to 2 cm and blades to 36 × 18 cm). Upper surface glossy, veins distinct and slightly raised above, prominent below, with 5–8 pairs of lateral veins. Inflorescence a head of flowers on a peduncle 0.5–2 cm long, opposite a leaf, with the subtending leaf on its side not developing, the flowers with calyx tubes fused to form a head, 1–3 cm across, with white flowers. Fruits compound, forming a syncarp, fused together by the calyx tubes, oblong to ovoid, 5–10 cm long, peduncle the same length, fruit wall 4 mm thick, warty, seeds ellipsoid, brown, 10 × 5 mm, in a white pulp attached to a central core of 1 cm thick, ripening greyish white, with a smell of rotting cheese.

Distribution and Habitat: Widely distributed as a wild plant along rocky coasts and lowlands from India, through Indochina, Malesia and the Pacific Islands. In Borneo, found along coasts and commonly planted in villages.
Vernacular Names: *mengkudu* (Malay); *engkudu* (Sarawak); noni fruit, Indian mulberry (English).
Notes: The fruits of this plant are made into a juice which is mainly taken as a tonic and was once commonly marketed as 'noni juice'. The ripe fruits are also eaten with sambal, while the young leaves are cooked as a vegetable. Many of the medicinal or health uses of the fruit and its juice are not known to be supported by scientific evidence, nevertheless, this species is still commonly grown in gardens and villages in Borneo. It was previously also useful for the dye that can be processed from its roots.

Flacourtia rukam Zoll. & Moritzi

Description: Small monoecious tree, 5–15 m, trunk with several stems from base, lower stems thorny (thorns to over 3 cm long). Base of lower or older branches also with spines. Twigs with alternate leaves in the same plane. Leaves simple, petioles glabrous, 7–10 mm, blades glabrous, ovate, elliptic to oblong-lanceolate, 4–10(–17) × 3–5(–9) cm, base rounded, apex long and obtuse, tip 1–2 cm, margins coarsely toothed especially towards apex, with 3–10 pairs of pinnate lateral veins. Inflorescences racemes on short stalks from leaf axils or on branches, with clusters of greenish-white male and female flowers. Fruits globose, berry slightly ridged, 2–2.5(–3) cm diameter, with red to reddish-purple, shiny, thin epicarp, a thick, juicy mesocarp, with several cream seeds to 6 × 6 × 3 mm. The edible pulp is usually sour, but becomes sweeter if the fruit is rubbed and bruised to stimulate chemical changes that bring out additional flavours and sweetness.

Distribution and Habitat: Throughout Malesia. An understorey tree in lowland and hill mixed dipterocarp forest to 500 m, less common in lower montane forest to 1800 m. Commonly cultivated around villages.
Vernacular Names: *rukam* (Malay).
Notes: The edible pulp has a good flavour and is often used for making jams and jellies.

Dimocarpus dentatus Meijer ex Leenh.

Description: Tree to 15–24 m tall, bole c. 5–8 m, sometimes with short buttresses. Leaves compound, pinnate, with 4–7 pairs of subopposite leaflets and no terminal leaflet, petiole and rachis 6–18 cm long, densely hairy. Leaflets oblong-obovate to lanceolate, petiolules 1–3 mm long, blade 5.5–24 cm × 3.2–9 cm, apex acute, base cuneate to obtuse to cordate in lower leaflets, margins dentate to serrate, rarely distantly and weakly dentate to undulate. Midvein flat above, with 10–20 pairs of impressed (sunken) lateral veins, midvein and lateral veins prominent on lower surface, with glands in the axils of the lateral veins and along the leaf margins. Inflorescence a panicle 25–55 cm long, with a few branches to 20 cm and shorter branches, bearing many sessile cymes with a few white flowers in cluster. Fruit a sub-globose drupe, 1.6 × 1.5 cm, epicarp green, glabrous, with large flat warts. Seed with shiny brown testa to 1 cm, and translucent, sweet, edible arillode.

Distribution and Habitat: Endemic to Borneo (Sabah and north and east Kalimantan only). Lowland and hill mixed dipterocarp forest, often along streams and rivers, or flood plains, as an understorey tree, to 300 m elevation, with a record for 750 m. Sometimes in secondary forest. It does seem to be cultivated, and trees near villages are from seeds discarded from forest-collected fruits.

Notes: The photographs here show fruits from trees in Sabah, which have leaflets with margins that are wavy rather than dentate.

Dimocarpus fumatus (Blume) Leenh. ssp. fumatus

Description: Tree 20–30 m tall, bole 2–8 m, sometimes with small buttresses, and a dense branching system. Leaves compound, pinnate, with 2–3(–4) pairs of leaflets, petiole and rachis to 15 cm long, hairy, stipules absent. Leaflets alternate to subopposite, petiolules 1.5–10 mm and grooved above. Blades elliptic to oblong, 6.5–28 × 2.5–10.5 cm, glabrous above, with sparsely hairy midvein and lateral veins below, apex acuminate, base cuneate to rounded (rarely asymmetric), margin entire to distantly dentate, midvein slightly raised above to prominent below, 10–20 pairs of lateral veins, with glands in the axils of the veins and along the leaflet margins. Inflorescence panicles to 50 cm with branches, terminal on the twigs or from the axils of upper pinnate leaves, with numerous flowers in cymes, greenish-white to cream, scented. Fruit a unilocular, globose drupe, 2–3.5 cm diameter, the thin epicarp glabrous but warty (rarely small spines), greenish- to yellowish-brown when ripe. Seed globose, 1–1.5 cm diameter, with dark brown testa, covered in a translucent to white arillode, 3 mm thick, that is sweet and tasty.

Distribution and Habitat: Indochina to southeast China and Peninsular Malaysia, Sumatra, Java, Philippines and Borneo. Understorey tree in lowland to hill mixed dipterocarp forest, both in alluvial plains, to hill slopes and ridge tops. Often along rivers and streams, and up to lower montane forest at 1300 m. Often cultivated for its fruits.

Vernacular Names: *mata kucing hutan* (Malay); *balabau* or *ribau* (Iban); *membuakat* (Sabah).

Notes: This subspecies, *fumatus*, occurs in Borneo, while there are other subspecies which occur in Sumatra and Java (ssp. *javensis*) (Radlk) Leenh. and Philippines (ssp. *philippinensis* Leenh.).

Dimocarpus longan Lour. ssp. malesianus Leenh. var. echinatus Leenh.

Description: Similar to var. *malesianus*. Leaves pinnate, with 1–4 pairs of leaflets, petiole and rachis 6–9 cm long, petiolules 3–15 mm, blade of leaflets elliptic to obovate, 4–22 × 1.5–9 cm, hairy or glabrous, glands present or absent. Inflorescence as in var. *malesianus*. Fruits globose, 1.5–3.5 cm diameter, with flattened spines 0.6–1 cm long forming a dense cover, ripening yellow to orange with brown tips to the spines. Arillode translucent, edible, sweet, juicy.

Distribution and Habitat: Only found in Philippines and Borneo (north Kalimantan and Sabah only). In lowland mixed dipterocarp forest, usually on alluvial and sandy soils, to 250 m. Also in secondary forest.

Vernacular Names: *mata kucing* (Malay); spiny longan (English).

Notes: This variety has good potential for selection and breeding as it has attractive fruits. It is not commonly cultivated in Sabah.

Dimocarpus longan Lour. ssp. malesianus Leenh. var. malesianus Leenh.

Description: Tree to 30 m, bole 2–10 m, buttresses up to 2 m high, with a dense, rounded crown. Leaves compound, pinnate, with 2–4 (rarely 6) pairs of leaflets and no terminal leaflet, opposite to alternate, petiole and rachis 13–30 cm long, hairy, stipules absent. Leaflets have petiolules 0.2–3.5 cm long, and often grooved above, blade elliptic to lanceolate, 3–45 × 1.8–30 cm, apex obtuse to acute, base oblique to rounded, slightly hairy, margin entire. Midvein sunken above, prominent below with secondary veins which vary from 10–20 pairs, with hairy tufts in axils with the midvein. Inflorescence a variable panicle 8–40 cm long, branched, with dense, woolly, greenish to white, scented flowers. Fruit a unilocular, globose drupe, 1–2.2 × 1–2 cm, with smooth to warty epicarp that is green or golden-brown to brown. Seed shiny brown, globose, 7–10 mm, covered by an arillode that is translucent to white, sweet, and juicy with distinct aroma.

Distribution and Habitat: Myanmar, Laos, Cambodia and south Vietnam, to Sumatra, Peninsular Malaysia, Philippines, Sulawesi, Moluccas and Borneo. In lowland mixed dipterocarp forest and secondary forest on many soil types, often along streams, hill slopes and ridges up to 600 m.

Vernacular Names: *mata kucing* (Malay); *isau, kakus, gurung* (Iban); *buku* (Kalimantan); longan (English).

Notes: *Dimocarpus longan* ssp. *malesianus* var. *malesianus* is very variable in both its leaves and fruits, with probably over 30–40 forms or varieties that are recognised by the different tribes in Borneo, but only four of which are commonly cultivated with their own local names. It is often cultivated as a fruit tree, and the fruits are sold in markets. Selected cultivars from Thailand are now also being planted. Another subspecies, *Dimocarpus longan* ssp. *longan*, appears not to be native in Borneo, but it has become naturalised and is also often cultivated.

Glenniea philippinensis (Radlk.) Leenh.

Family Sapindaceae

无患子科

菲律宾荔枝

Description: Tree 15–18(–25) m, bole c. 5 m with small buttresses. Leaves spirally arranged, pinnate, petioles 3–9 cm long, with 3–6 pairs of opposite leaflets and no terminal leaflet, petiolules 2–4(–10) mm, grooved, with no stipules. Blade ovate to elliptic to oblong (some obovate), with 10–12 pairs of lateral veins, upper surface glabrous, midvein and veins on lower surface with hairs. Inflorescences terminal or pseudo-terminal panicles from leaf axils, with dense, small white flowers. Fruits globose, some slightly pear-shaped, epicarp glabrous, green to yellow when ripe. Mesocarp yellow, sweet, edible but leaving a soapy texture, containing 2 ovoid seeds, 1.7–2.5 × 1.5–2 cm, with hard brown endocarp and no arillode.

Distribution & Habitat: Southeast Thailand, Vietnam, Philippines, Peninsular Malaysia and Borneo (Sabah only). In Sabah, very rare in mixed hill forest 300–800 m on sandstone formations.
Notes: The local Murut tribes in Sabah did not know of this fruit, probably because it is so rare. Wild boars were observed eating the fruit, which was probably originally distributed by rhinoceros (now nearly extinct in the wild).

Lepisanthes alata (Blume) Leenh.

Description: Monoecious treelet to small tree, 5–15 m tall, leaves pinnate with 5–13 pairs of usually sessile leaflets. Petiole including the rachis winged, 5–25 cm long, with at least 2 pairs of leaflet-like pseudo-stipules at the base. Leaflets opposite to alternate, often sessile or with petiolules to 2 mm, linear to lanceolate to oblong, 10–20 × 1.8–4 cm but sometimes longer, base acute, apex acute to long pointed (attenuate). Inflorescences mostly pendulous along the twigs, with male flowers on unbranched inflorescences to 25 cm long, and female inflorescences strongly branched to 45 cm. Flowers wine-red to purple. Fruits with pedicels 0.5–2 cm, ovoid to obovoid drupe (slightly three lobed) 2–4 × 2–3 cm, apex of fruit apiculate. Epicarp thick, turning from green to purple to red when ripe, shiny, glabrous. Seeds two per fruit, ellipsoid, to 2.5 × 1.5 covered in a thick white pulp that is sweet.

Distribution and Habitat: Endemic to Borneo, but more common in Sabah, rarer in Brunei and Sarawak. Found in secondary and primary mixed hill forest up to 1000 m.

Vernacular Names: *ceri* (Malay); *engkili* (Iban).

Notes: The tree is also grown as an ornamental, and the fruits are also used for feeding fish.

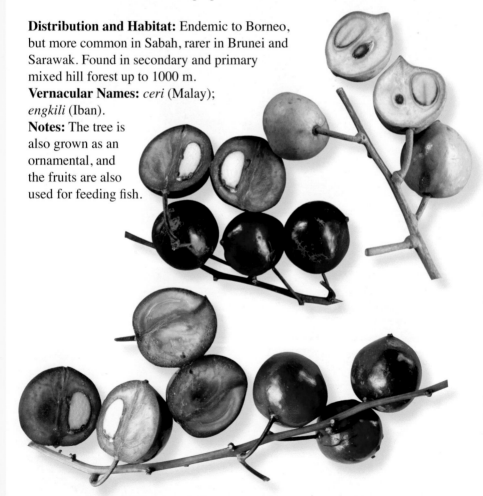

Lepisanthes multijuga (Hook.f.) Leenh.

Description: Shrub to tree, 5–12 m, often with several stems, leaves pinnate, with 12–30 pairs of sessile leaflets with a terminal leaflet. Petiole including rachis 55–60 cm, the basal petiole 3–6 cm, with 1 or 2 pairs of leaflet-like pseudo-stipules at the base. Leaflets sessile, linear to lanceolate with long pointed (attenuate) apex and rounded base, mostly opposite, 10–14(–18) × 2–2.5(–3) cm. Inflorescence terminal 25–30 cm, branching with reddish flowers. Fruits with 3 lobes but often only 1 lobe develops, ellipsoid, 2–3 cm long × 1.3–2 cm. Epicarp thin, yellow to brownish orange when ripe. Seeds 1–2 per fruit, brown, obconic, with white endosperm, 12 × 9 mm, and with a translucent, sweet, thin, edible mesocarp.

Distribution and Habitat: Endemic to Borneo—Sabah, rare in Brunei and Sarawak. Found in secondary and primary mixed hill forest up to 1000 m.
Notes: It is not well-known in Sabah except by local communities who are hunter-gatherers. It is not cultivated as far as is known.

Nephelium cuspidatum Blume

Description: Tree to 40 m, bole 3–6 m with small buttresses. Leaves compound, pinnate, spirally arranged, petiole and rachis hairy, with no pseudo-stipules, 3–21 cm, sometimes with grooved petiole with 2–9–13 pairs of leaflets. Leaflets with petiolules 2–7.5–15 mm long, flat to grooved above, blades narrowly elliptic to oblong, 6–35 × 1.75–12.5 cm, apex rounded to acute, but mostly acuminate, base cuneate to rounded, upper surface glabrous, sometimes with hairs on the slightly raised or sunken midvein, lower surface veins prominent, whole surface pale whitish green, hairy, domatia absent. Each leaflet with 7–20 pairs of lateral veins, mostly close together and sunken on the upper surface. Inflorescence a large, branched panicle, sometimes terminal to pseudo-terminal in the upper leaf axils, rarely pendulous spikes or racemes on leafless twigs or stems. Female flowers have spikes of pink and white flowers. Fruits ellipsoid to globose, 2–4 × 2–3 cm, glabrous, densely covered in ligulate to filiform appendages 0.6–2 cm long depending on the variety. Fruit coat (epicarp) and appendages usually red to yellowish-red. Seeds covered in white, sweet to sour, juicy, edible sarcotesta, seed with fibrous endocarp 1.5–2 cm long.

Distribution and Habitat: Myanmar, Thailand, Cambodia, Vietnam, Peninsular Malaysia, Sumatra, west Java, southern Philippines and Borneo. Three varieties and 2 sub-varieties are recorded for Borneo, out of a total of 6 varieties and 3 sub-varieties. Many are in cultivation. An understorey tree in lowland to hill mixed dipterocarp and secondary forest, seldom riverine, mainly on ridges and hill slopes, rare on limestone soils.
Vernacular Names: *rambutan hutan* (Malay); *buah sibau* (Iban).
Notes: Forest trees often have sour fruits, but over time, sweet-fruited varieties were also found in the forest, and have become popular and cultivated on a wide scale, with their fruits sold in markets (but not on the scale of the common rambutan).

The Bornean varieties are illustrated in the following pages.

1. *N. cuspidatum* var. *cuspidatum* Blume
Leaflets less than 35 cm long and narrower, 1.75–5 cm. Inflorescences pseudo-terminal. Fruits with short, straight to curved appendages, 5–6 mm long.

2. *N. cuspidatum* **var.** *robustum* (Radlk.) Leenh.
Leaflets 35 × 5–10 cm. Inflorescences terminal. Large fruits with curled appendages 1.5–2 cm long.

4. *N. cuspidatum* var. *eriopetalum* (Miq.) Leenh.
Leaflets to 20–35 × 3–12.5 cm. Inflorescences terminal or pseudo-terminal.
Fruits with straight to curled appendages 1–2 cm long.

Nephelium lappaceum L.

Description: Tree 20–40 m tall, bole 3–6 m, sometimes fluted, buttresses 1.5–2(–4) m tall, broadly globular crown. Leaves compound pinnate, spirally arranged, petiole and rachis 2–10(–16) cm long, with no pseudo stipules, hairy to glabrous, shallowly grooved, with 1–3(–5) pairs of leaflets. Leaflets with petiolules 2–10 mm, shallowly grooved, blade ovate to obovate, 5–28 × 2–10.5 cm, apex truncate to acuminate, base cuneate to rounded, glabrous above, midvein sometimes with hairs, with 6–10 pairs of lateral veins, mostly hairy on the lower surface, domatia (glands) present or absent. Inflorescence terminal to pseudo-terminal branching panicle, to 50 cm, with white flowers (trees either dioecious with male flowers only, or monoecious with male and female flowers). Fruits ellipsoid to sub-globular, glabrous, unilocular drupe, 3–5(–7) × 2–3.5(–5) cm, epicarp 2.5–3 mm thick, yellow to red to purplish-red, with dense green to yellow to red, filiform, curved appendages, 0.5–2 cm. Seed flattened, to 2 cm long with fibrous hard endocarp, covered in a white, thick, juicy, sweet to sour, edible sarcotesta.

Distribution and Habitat: Southern China, Indochina, Thailand, Peninsular Malaysia, Sumatra, Java, Sulawesi, Philippines and Borneo. Understorey tree in lowland to hill mixed dipterocarp forest to 600 m. Widespread in cultivation with many selected clones.

Vernacular Names: *rambutan* (Malay); *sunggau* (Iban).

Notes: Three varieties are recognised in Borneo, with var. *xanthioides* (Radlk.) Leenh. endemic to Borneo, which has broad leaflets to 10 cm, widest at the middle, acuminate apex with curved sides, and fruits 3 × 2 cm. It is commonly cultivated in Sarawak. Var. *pallens* (Hiern) Leenh. has narrow leaflets 3–4 cm widest below the middle, glabrous beneath, margins mainly parallel, and fruits to 5 × 3.5 cm. In var. *lappaceum* the leaflets are widest above the middle, with strongly curved lateral veins and margins, and an acute or blunt apex, and the fruits are the largest, to 6.5 × 3.5 cm.

Nephelium maingayi Hiern

Description: Tree to 40 m, bole 6–10 m, sometimes with buttresses to 1.4 m high. Leaves, compound, pinnate, spirally arranged, petiole and rachis to 10 cm, mostly glabrous, with no pseudo-stipules, often with 2–3 pairs of leaflets (rarely five). Leaflets with petiolules 4–17 mm, grooved, leaflets subopposite to alternate, elliptic to obovate, 5.75–22 × 2.75–9 cm, apex obtuse to acute, base cuneate to rounded, margin entire, upper surface glabrous, sometimes with hairs on midvein which is normally impressed (sunken), the 6–9 pairs of curving lateral veins also impressed above, midvein and lateral veins prominent and hairy on the lower surface, glands (domatia) absent. Inflorescence axillary to terminal on twigs, a compact panicle in the form of a cylindrical cyme, flowers with no petals. Fruit unilocular or drupe-like, ellipsoid with flattened sides, 2–3.75 cm long × 1.25–1.75 cm wide × 1–1.25 cm thick, pedicel (stalk) 2–3 mm, with a remnant of the style forming a hook above the stalk, epicarp glabrous, 1–1.5 mm thick with folds and grooves, ripening bright red, sarcotesta edible, with fibres around the seed, white, juicy, sweet to sour.

Distribution and Habitat: Peninsular Malaysia, Sumatra and Borneo. In lowland and hill mixed dipterocarp forest, from flood plains, to hills and ridges, and also in peat swamps, to medium altitudes to 700 m, rarer in upper hill to lower montane forest up to 1600 m. Also in secondary forest, sometimes cultivated.

Vernacular Names: *serait* (Malay); *mujau* (Iban); *buah sungkit* (Sabah and Brunei).

Notes: A very distinct species based on its glabrous, warty fruits, leaves with no domatia (glands), and flowers without petals. Fruits are mostly collected from the forest and sold in rural markets.

Nephelium papillatum Leenh.

Description: Tree to 36 m, bole to 5 m, with buttresses to 2 m high. Leaves compound, pinnate with 2–3 pairs of leaflets, sub-opposite, petiole and rachis 2–5 cm long, with no stipules. Leaflets with petiolules 5–8 mm long, grooved, blade glabrous, elliptic, 4.5–10.5 × 2.5–4.5 cm, apex obtuse to acuminate, base cuneate to obtuse, midvein flat to slightly sunken, with 6–8 pairs of lateral veins, slightly raised, slightly prominent on the lower surface. No glands (domatia). Inflorescence a panicle, axillary on twigs to pseudo-terminal, with small white to cream flowers. Fruits ellipsoid, 2.25 × 1.75 cm, the epicarp covered in dense, glabrous, pyramidal, dark red, nipple-like appendages to 2 mm long, sarcotesta around flattish seed with fibres, white, juicy, sweet, edible, but in small quantity. Seed with fibrous endocarp, c. 1.3 cm × 8 mm × 5 mm.

Distribution and Habitat: Endemic to Borneo (Sabah only). In mixed hill to lower montane forest from 600–1300 m which is rich in oaks and chestnuts (Fagaceae species). Not cultivated, but trees can be found around villages where seeds have been discarded from fruits collected from the forest.

Notes: This is a fairly uncommon tree, the fruits only gathered from forest trees, and consumed back in the villages.

Nephelium ramboutan-ake (Labill) Leenh.

Description: Medium tree 10–20–30 m, bole 3–5 m, buttresses up to 2.4 m, with a dense, rounded crown. Leaves compound, pinnate, petiole and rachis 1–12 cm, no pseudo-stipules, with 1–3(–7) pairs of leaflets (often 3 in Borneo). Leaflets with petiolules 3–8 mm long, grooved, blade elliptic, 4–20 × 2–11 cm, apex acuminate, base cuneate to rounded. Upper surface glabrous, midvein usually slightly prominent, sometimes with hairs, lower surface covered in closely appressed soft hairs, but often glabrous in Borneo, glands (domatia) sometimes present, midvein and 7–12 pairs of secondary veins prominent on both surfaces. Inflorescence panicles that are pseudo-terminal but mostly axillary near the ends of twigs in Borneo, with small, greenish-white flowers. Fruits ellipsoid to sub-globular, 4–6.5 × 2.5–5 cm, glabrous, covered in appendages to 5 mm tall, creating an epicarp (rind) 7 mm thick. The knobby rind of the fruit, when ripe, is commonly purple-black to reddish purple, but green and yellow forms also exist. Sarcotesta around the seed with few fibres, is translucent white, very juicy, sweet to sour. Seed ovoid, 2–3 cm long, with a hard, fibrous endocarp, and edible endosperm if cooked. Seeds can be roasted and used to make a 'cocoa'-like drink.

Distribution and Habitat: Myanmar, Thailand, Malay Peninsula and Sumatra have a common distinct form, whereas Philippines and Borneo have their distinct form. In lowland and hill dipterocarp forest on different soils, understorey tree often near rivers, to 1500 m. Also in secondary forest, cultivated on a wide scale, and becoming popular.

Vernacular Names: *pulasan* (Malay); *maritam* (Sabah and Brunei); *mua* or *mak* (Iban).

Note: This species is still often referred to as *N. mutabile* Blume. This is a common tree which is very variable in fruit. Many good varieties have been selected and are now in cultivation and commonly sold in markets.

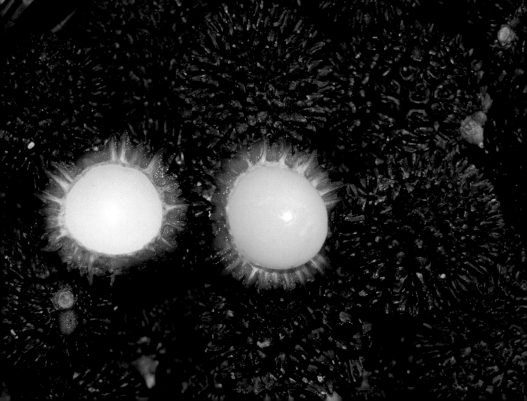

Pometia pinnata J.R. Forst. & G. Forst.

Description: Very variable tree, 20–50 m, bole to 5–10 m, spreading, tall buttresses to 5 m high on older trees, a broad canopy, with spirally arranged, large, pinnate leaves, often in whorls at the ends of branches, new flushes of leaves a deep red. Leaves pinnate to 1 m long, with 4–13 opposite to alternate, sub-sessile leaflets. Petiole-rachis with swollen base, with small pseudo-stipule-like leaflets, glabrous to hairy. Leaflets ovate to obovate, basal and apical leaflets smaller, petiolules 1.5–4 mm, blades 6–32 × 2–13 cm, margins entire to broadly dentate, apex acute to acuminate, base rounded, midvein and lateral veins impressed (sunken) on upper surface, glabrous to variably hairy, and variably glandular, on the lower surface. Inflorescences panicles from leaf axils, erect to drooping, 15–70 cm long, hairy, with cream to white coloured flowers. Fruit a drupe, ovoid to nearly globose, 1.5–3(–5) × 1–3 cm, epicarp, glabrous, thin leathery, yellowish green to red or black when ripe, mesocarp thick, juicy, semi-transparent to white, edible and sweet. Part of the mesocarp around the seed is in fact a thin, fleshy arillode. Seed ovoid, reddish-brown, to 2.5 × 1.5 cm.

Distribution and Habitat: Throughout Malesia and Pacific islands. Understorey or stream and riverside tree in primary and secondary lowland to hill forests, to 1500 m. Also in swamp forests and flood plains.
Vernacular Names: *kasai* (malay); *silik* or *enselan* (Iban).
Notes: It appears to be more widely cultivated in New Guinea and the Pacific islands, where there are varieties with larger sweet fruits. In Borneo, it is very variable, with yellow-green to reddish and purple fruits. Some forms have a thicker, sweet aril and are cultivated in illages, or are collected from trees along rivers.

Alpinia nieuwenhuizii Valeton

Description: Perennial herb, with branching stems (rhizomes) in the top soil forming clumps of tall, leafy shoots to 2–3.5 m. Pseudostem with a swollen base, leaf sheaths with a finely reticulate surface, and short ligules 0.5–1.5 cm, leaf blades glabrous, alternate, laterally arranged, with a distinct petiole, elliptic to oblong with acuminate apex and cuneate base. Inflorescence a terminal, lax, panicle, with long basal branches with many flowers, the flowers with a large or distinct lip with a central white band, and edges banded red and cream. Fruits globose, edible, capsular with 3 locules, green to red when young, ripening yellow, with small seeds in a whitish aril, slightly sour to sweet.

Distribution and Habitat: Endemic to Borneo. In lowland and hill mixed dipterocarp forest to 1000 m, often along rivers where there is more light, and in secondary forest. Not often cultivated.

Vernacular Names: *lalemas* (Iban); *terebak* (Sabah).

Notes: The lowland form of this species is a larger plant with larger flowers. The fruits are generally eaten by hunter-gatherers. The shoots are also eaten as a vegetable.

Etlingera coccinea (Blume) S. Sakai & Nagam.

Description: Perennial herb, with long, creeping underground branching stem (rhizome) to 3 cm diameter, giving rise to leafy shoots (pseudostems) usually 2–4 m tall in cultivation in sunny conditions, to 6–8 m tall in the forest, forming a cluster, with a swollen base to 8 cm diameter. Leaf sheaths glabrous to pubescent with ciliate margin, ending in an entire ligule, joined to a sessile leaf blade. Blades arranged in alternate lateral rows, with 8–14 pairs of glabrous leaflets, oblong to obovate, 70–110 × 6–20 cm, apex acuminate, base cuneate. Inflorescence mostly covered by soil, peduncle 2–12 cm from the rhizome, with an ovate spike or head of flowers, 5–6 cm tall, with a basal dense cluster of 5–10 sterile fertile bracts 4.5–6 cm × 0.7–0.9 cm above soil level, with 5 or more flowers open at a time, 2–3 cm above the soil. Flowers with bright scarlet corolla tubes, and scarlet and yellow labellum. Fruits forming an ovate head 12 cm across, with 5–12 pyriform fruits, 4 cm long and 3.5 cm across, flat on top with radiating, irregular ridges, reddish-brown when ripe, with many seeds 2–3 mm diameter, in white, aromatic aril, arranged in 3 locules.

Distribution and Habitat: Thailand, Peninsular Malaysia, Sumatra, Java and Borneo. In lowland and hill mixed dipterocarp forest, heath forest, on river banks in forest gaps and secondary forest, and commonly cultivated in villages.

Vernacular Names: *tepus* (Iban); *tuhau* (Sabah).

Notes: Some wild forms with stems 6–8 m tall lack the aroma in the central leaf sheath of the cultivated form. The central leafy shoots and inflorescences are commonly sold in the markets as condiments, often in jars, pickled in vinegar, with chillies and onions. The fruits are edible and eaten raw or cooked as a condiment, with a similar flavour and aroma as its central leafy shoot and inflorescence.

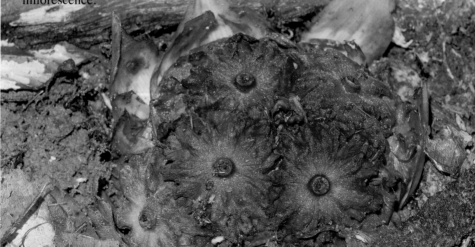

Etlingera elatior (Jack) R.M. Sm.

Description: Perennial herb, the stem or rhizome short, creeping in the top soil, the leafy shoots (pseudostem) 2–6 m tall, forming a loose clump, with up to 14–34 laterally arranged leaves, arising from green leaf sheaths, with an apical, entire ligule 1–1.2 cm, joined by the petioles 1.3–2.5 cm long. Blade is glabrous, oblong, to 80 × 20 cm, apex acuminate, base truncate. Inflorescence with peduncle 1–2 m tall, erect from the rhizome near to the base of the leaf shoot, bearing a conical head or spike 13 × 12 cm, with basal red bracts and up to 300 flowers with red labellum with yellow margin. Inflorescence remains erect, the fruiting head is 10–12 × 5–9 cm, with 50–100 fruits. Fruits each 2.5–3.5 × 1.5–2.5 cm, pyriform, the top rounded, ripening pale orange to reddish-pink. Fruit exocarp and pericarp enclosing many round seeds, 4 mm diameter, in 3 locules, surrounded by a sweet aril.

Distribution and Habitat: Thailand, Peninsular Malaysia, Sumatra, Java, Sulawesi and Borneo. Varieties with white or pale pink flowers have been introduced to Borneo. In the lowland forests, it is common along river banks and secondary forest where there is more light, and it is often also found in hill forest, and has also been recorded from peatswamp and limestone forest. Commonly cultivated in villages and urban areas.

Vernacular Names: *kantan* (Malay); *ckekala* (Iban); torch ginger (English).

Notes: The fruits are eaten fresh, and are also used in curries. The young inflorescence is used to flavour dishes such as Penang laksa. Although the species has been recorded in the wild in very remote localities all over Borneo, especially in Kalimantan, its origin cannot be confirmed, as people have been moving all over Borneo for hundreds of years, and usually plant this species in their villages.

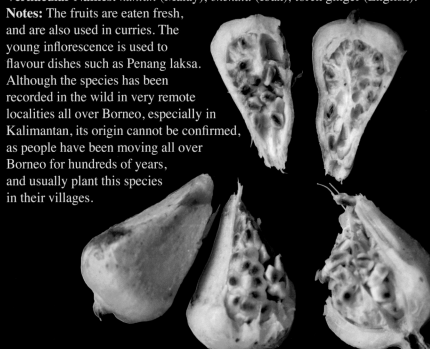

Hornstedtia havilandii (K. Schum.) K. Schum.

Description: Perennial herb, with a branching stem or rhizome at or just above ground level on short stilt roots, forming a clump of closely-spaced leafy shoots or pseudostems, 3–4 m tall, with a swollen base to 5 cm. Basal leaf sheaths finely reticulate with entire ligule, short petiole, and 6–10 alternate, elliptic, laterally arranged, oblong blades, with acuminate apex, and obtuse base. Inflorescence arising directly from the rhizome, close to the base of the pseudostem, with tall peduncle, covered by green to reddish bracts with fine reticulations, 20–40 cm tall, topped by a spindle-shaped, fusiform flower spike, covered in larger, sterile, reticulate bracts, with one or two flowers opening one at a time from the top of the spike. Flowers red with a white lip. The fruits develop hidden by the bracts, making the spike become much enlarged. Ripe fruits covered by thin, papery bracts, with a thin epicarp which is cream to pale yellow, oblong, 3 × 1.5 cm, and contains many small, black seeds, in a cream to translucent white aril, which is edible, sweet and juicy, with a delicious passionfruit flavour, and can be eaten raw.

Distribution and Habitat: Endemic to Borneo. A widespread species in lowland to hill mixed dipterocarp forest, and riverine forest up to 1000 m. Not commonly cultivated.

Vernacular Names: *panyun* (Iban); *telidus* (Sabah).

Notes: The young shoots are also cooked as a vegetable. It has one of the tastiest fruits of the many edible wild ginger species, similar to *H. scyphifera* (J. Koenig) Steud.

Illustrated Glossary of Botanical Terms

Types of Plants

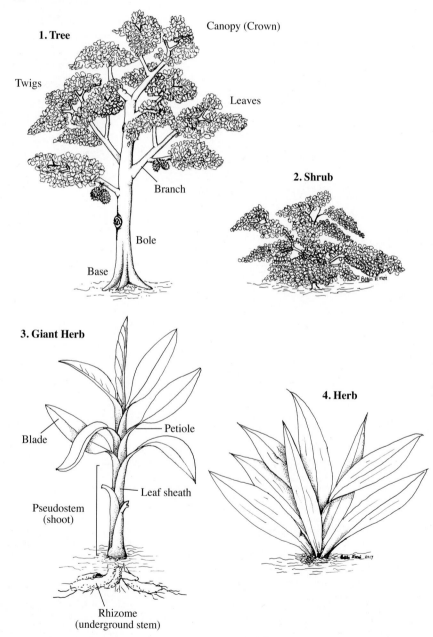

1. Tree

Canopy (Crown)

Twigs

Leaves

Branch

Bole

Base

2. Shrub

3. Giant Herb

Blade

Petiole

Leaf sheath

Pseudostem (shoot)

4. Herb

Rhizome (underground stem)

2. Tree Bases

Columnar base

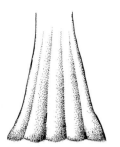

Fluted base

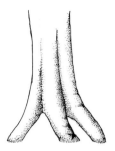

Buttressed base

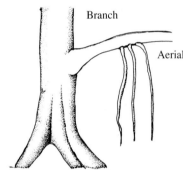

Branch

Aerial roots

Stilt roots (Prop roots)

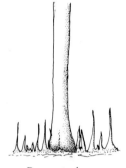

Pneumatophores
(Breathing roots)

3. Fruiting Bodies

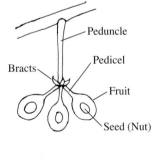

Peduncle

Bracts

Pedicel

Fruit

Seed (Nut)

Infructescence
(Fruiting body)

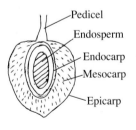

Pedicel

Endosperm

Endocarp

Mesocarp

Epicarp

Pericarp

A Fruit

4. Types of Leaf

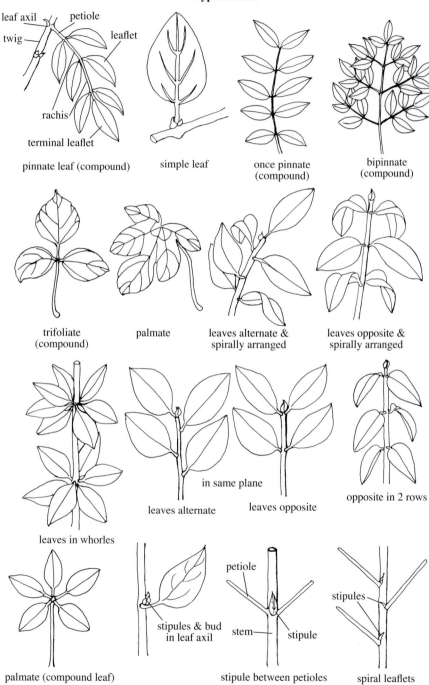

leaf axil · petiole · twig · leaflet · rachis · terminal leaflet
pinnate leaf (compound)

simple leaf

once pinnate (compound)

bipinnate (compound)

trifoliate (compound)

palmate

leaves alternate & spirally arranged

leaves opposite & spirally arranged

leaves in whorles

leaves alternate

in same plane

leaves opposite

opposite in 2 rows

palmate (compound leaf)

stipules & bud in leaf axil

petiole · stem · stipule
stipule between petioles

stipules
spiral leaflets

4. Leaf Type

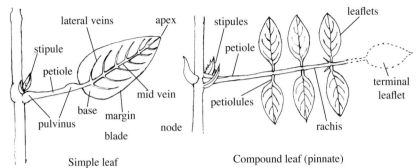

Simple leaf

Compound leaf (pinnate)

5. Petiole cross section

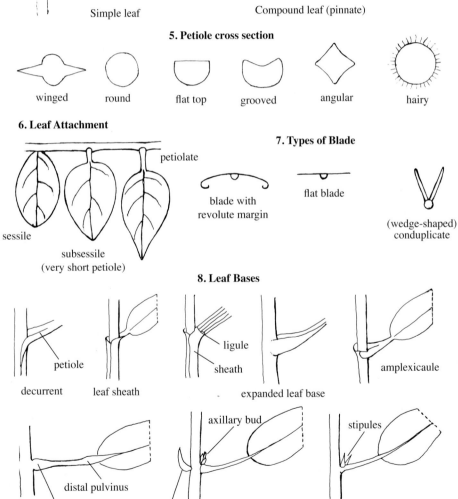

winged   round   flat top   grooved   angular   hairy

6. Leaf Attachment

7. Types of Blade

petiolate

blade with revolute margin

flat blade

(wedge-shaped) conduplicate

sessile

subsessile (very short petiole)

8. Leaf Bases

petiole

decurrent   leaf sheath

ligule

sheath

expanded leaf base

amplexicaule

distal pulvinus

axillary bud

stipules

proximal pulvinus   interpetiolar stipule

Leaf Shape

  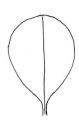  

broadly ovate   obovate   elliptic   narrowly elliptic   asymmetric lanceolate

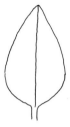  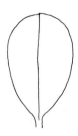  

ovate   lanceolate   broadly obovate   narrowly obovate   linear

   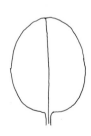 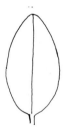

orbicular   spathulate   cordate   oval   elliptic lanceolate

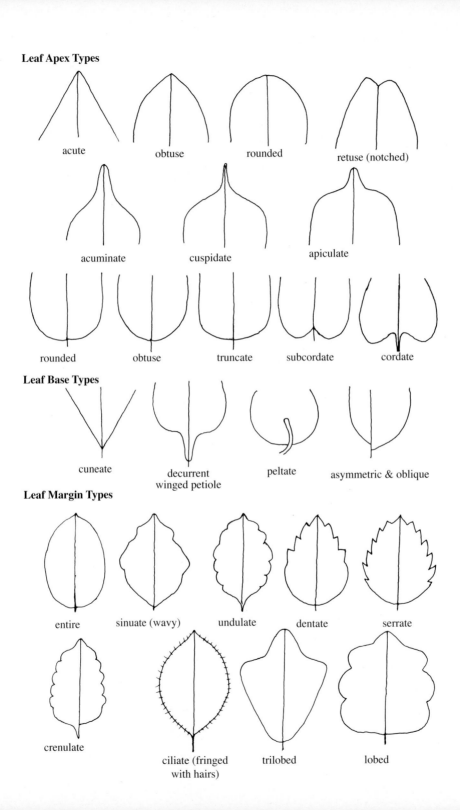

Leaf Apex Types

acute obtuse rounded retuse (notched)

acuminate cuspidate apiculate

rounded obtuse truncate subcordate cordate

Leaf Base Types

cuneate decurrent winged petiole peltate asymmetric & oblique

Leaf Margin Types

entire sinuate (wavy) undulate dentate serrate

crenulate ciliate (fringed with hairs) trilobed lobed

Inflorescences

single

simple

cyme

compound cyme

spike

raceme

corymb

umbel

panicle

Flowers
bisexual

unisexual male

unisexual female

Fruits
Berry with
single seed

Berry
multiple
seeds

1-seeded
drupe (e.g.
mango)

3-seeded
drupe (e.g.
Canarium)

Aggregate fruit
(many drupes)
e.g. Raspberry

Aggregate
fruit e.g. *Morinda*

Compound fruit
(syncarp) e.g.
Artocarpus

Compound fruit
(Syconia) e.g. *Ficus*

Nut with 1 seed
(e.g. *Castanopsis
megacarpa*)

Nut with 3
seeds (e.g.
*Castanopsis
foxworthyi*)

Nut with
wings (e.g.
Shorea)

Follicle
(e.g. *Sterculia
foetida*)

Capsular fruit
with locules
(e.g. *Durio*)

Legume pod
(e.g. *Parkia*)

References & Further Reading

Adema, F., Leenhouts, P.W. & van Welzen, P.C. (1994). Sapindaceae. *Flora Malesiana*, Series I, Vol. II, Part 3.

Anderson, J.A.R. (1983). The Flora of the peat swamp forests of Sarawak & Brunei. *Gardens' Bulletin Singapore* 29: 131–228.

Argent G. et al. (1997). *Manuals of the Larger and More Important Non-Dipterocarp Trees of Central Kalimantan, Indonesia*. Vols. 1 & 2. Forest Research Institute, Samarinda.

Ashton, P.S. (1982). Dipteroacarpaceae. In: *Flora Malesiana* 1(9). ed. C.J.J. G. van Steenis, pp. 237–552. Martinus Nijhoff Publishers, The Hague.

Ashton, P.S. (2004). Dipterocarpaceae. In: *Tree Flora of Sabah & Sarawak, Vol. 5*. ed. E. Soepadmo, Saw, L.G. & R.C.K. Chung, pp. 63–388. Forest Research Institute Malaysia (F.R.I.M.), Kepong.

Ashton, P.S. (2014). *On the Forests of Tropical Asia*. Royal Botanic Gardens Kew.

Beaman, J.H. & Anderson, C. (2004). *The Plants of Kinabalu. Vol. 5. Dicotyledon families Magnoliaceae to Winteraceae*. Natural History Publications (Borneo), Kota Kinabalu.

Beaman, J.H. & Beaman, R.S. (1998). *The Plants of Mount Kinabalu. Vol. 3, Gymnosperms and Non-Orchid Monocotyledons*. Natural History Publications (Borneo), Kota Kinabalu.

Beaman, J.H., Anderson, C. & Beaman, R.S. (2001). *The Plants of Mount Kinabalu, Vol. 4. Dicotyledon families Acanthaceae to Lythraceae*. Natural History Publications (Borneo), Kota Kinabalu.

Beaman, R.S., Beaman, J.H., Marsh, C.W. & Woods, P.V. (1985). Drought and Forest Fires in Sabah in 1983. *Sabah Society Journ. 8:10–30*.

Berg, C.C. & Corner, E.J.H. (2005). Moraceae (*Ficus*). *Flora Malesiana*. Series I, Vol. 17, Pt. 2. Nationaal Herbarium Nederland, Leiden.

Berg, C.C., Corner, E.J.H. & Jarrett, F.M. (2006). Moraceae (genera other than *Ficus*). *Flora Malesiana*, Series I, Vol. 17. Pt. 1. Nationaal Herbarium Nederland.

Brunig, E.F. (1974). *Ecological Studies in the Heath Forests of Sarawak and Brunei*. Borneo Literature Bureau, Kuching.

Burkill, I.H. (1966). *A Dictionary of the Economic Products of the Malay Peninsula*. 2nd ed. 2 volumes. Ministry of Agriculture and Co-operatives, Kuala Lumpur.

Christensen, H. (2002). *Ethnobotany of the Iban and the Kelabit*, Forest Department Sarawak, NEPCon, Denmark, University of Aarhus, Denmark.

Cockburn, P.F. (1967 & 1980). *Trees of Sabah*. Vols. 1 & 2. Forest Department, Sabah.

Corner, E.J.H. (1988). *Wayside Trees of Malaya*. 3rd ed. Vols. 1 & 2. Malayan Nature Society, Kuala Lumpur.

Det, P.A., Yuon, L.C., Umar, S., Brooke, P., Razili, R.M., Ismani, H. & Meng, L.S. (2013). *Edible Wild Plants in Sarawak*. Research Division, Department of Agriculture, Sarawak.

Haegens, R.M.A.P. (2002). Taxonomy, Phylogeny and Biogeography of *Baccaurea*, *Distichirhops* & *Nothobaccaurea*. *Blumea* Supplement 12, Nationaal Herbarium Nederlands.

Hazebroek, H.P. & Morshidi, A.K.A. (2000). *National Parks of Sarawak*. Natural History Publications (Borneo), Kota Kinabalu.

Hazebroek, H.P., Adlin, T.Z.A. & Waidi, S. (2004). *Maliau Basin: Sabah's Lost World*. Natural History Publications (Borneo), Kota Kinabalu.

Hazebroek, H.P., Adlin, T.Z.A. & Waidi, S. (2012). *Danum Valley: The Rain Forest*. Natural History Publications (Borneo), Kota Kinabalu.

Khadijah, A., Khairulazhar, M.M., Nor, A.M., Razali, A., Rusli, O., Khairuddin, O.M., Sofiah, M. & Shukri, M.A.M. (2018). Diversity, distribution and conservation of *Baccaurea* species in the home gardens and orchards in Malaysia. *Malayan Nature Journal* 70(3): 333–339.

Kochummen, K.M. (1972). Bombacaceae. In: *Tree Flora of Malaya* (ed. T.C. Whitmore), Vol. 1: 100–116.

Kostermans, A.J.G.H. (1958). The genus *Durio* Adans. (Bombacaceae). *Reinwardtia* 4(3): 47–150.

Kostermans, A.J.G.H. & Bompard, J.M. (1993). *The Mangoes*. Academic Press Limited, London.

La Frankie, J.V. (2010). *Trees of Tropical Asia*. Black Tree Publications, Inc. Philippines.

Lamb, A., Januarius Gobilik, Marlina Ardiyani & Poulsen, A.D. (2013). *A Guide to Gingers of Borneo*. Natural History Publications (Borneo), Kota Kinabalu.

Mackinnon, K. et al. (1996). *The Ecology of Kalimantan*. Periplus Editions (HK) Ltd.

Meijaard, E. & Shiel, D. (2013). Oil palm plantations in the context of biodiversity conservation. In: *Encyclopaedia of Biodiversity*, 2nd ed. pp. 600–612. Elsevier.

Nilus, R., Chung, A.Y.C., Pereira, J.T., Sugau, J.B., Tangah, J., Sabran, S. & Chong, R.F.Y. (2010). *Mangroves of Sabah*. Sabah Forestry Department, Sandakan.

Payne, J.B. (2010). *Wild Sabah*. John Beaufoy Publishing Limited.

Primack, R.B (1983). *Foresters Guide to Moraceae of Sarawak*. Forest Department, Sarawak.

Richards, P.W. (1996). *The Tropical Rainforest*. Cambridge University Press.

Salma, I. (2011). *Durio of Malaysia*. Malaysian Agricultural Research and Development Institute (MARDI).

Saw, L.G., La Frankie, J.V., Kochumen, K.M. & Yap, S.K. (1991). Fruit Trees in a Malaysian Rainforest. *Economic Botany* 45(1): 120–136.

Serudin Tinggal (1992). *Brunei Darussalam Fruits in Colour*. University Brunei Darussalam.

Siong, K.H. (2003). *Indigenous Fruits of Sarawak*. Forest Department, Sarawak and International Tropical Timber Organisation (ITTO).

Tirtawinata, M.R. & Wicaksono, M.H. (2016). *Portret Buah Nusantara*. Peneber Swadaya, Perum.

Tree Flora of Sabah & Sarawak. Sabah Forestry Department, Forest Research Institute Malaysia and Sarawak Forestry Department — indicating those families shown in this guide.

a) Vol. 1. ed. Soepadmo, E. & Wong, K.M. (1995). Covering Alangiaceae (see Cornaceae), Burseraceae, Olacaceae, Oxalidaceae and Sonneratiaceae.

b) Vol. 2. ed. Soepadmo, E., Wong, K.M. & Saw, L.G. (1996). Covering Anacardiaceae, Malvaceae & Sapindaceae.

c) Vol. 3. ed. Soepadmo, E. & Saw, L.G. (2000). Covering Fagaceae, Moraceae & Leguminosae (see Fabaceae).

d) Vol. 4. ed. Soepadmo, E., Saw, L.G. & Chung, R.C.K. (2002). Covering Proteaceae.

e) Vol. 5. ed. Soepadmo, E., Saw, L.G. & Chung, R.C.K. (2004). Covering Apocynaceae & Dipterocarpaceae.

f) Vol. 6. ed. Soepadmo, E., Saw, L.G. & Chung, R.C.K. (2007). Covering Meliaceae & Polygalaceae.

g) Vol. 7. ed. Soepadmo, E., Saw, L.G., Chung, R.C.K. and Kiew, R. (2011). Covering Myrtaceae.

h) Vol. 8. ed Soepadmo, E., Saw, L.G., Chung, R.C.K. & Kiew, R. (2014). Covering Annonaceae.

Van der Ent, A. (2013). *Kinabalu*. Natural History Publications (Borneo), Kota Kinabalu.

Van der Ent, A., Repin, R., Sugau, J. & Wong, K.M. (2014). *The Ultramafic Flora of Sabah: An Introduction to the Plant Diversity on Ultramafic Soils*. Sabah Parks & Natural History Publications (Borneo), Kota Kinabalu.

Verheij, E.W.M. & Coronel, R.E. (eds.) (1991 & 1992). *Plant Resources of South-east Asia, no. 2. Edible Fruits & Nuts*, PROSEA, Bogor.

Voon, B.H. & Kueh, H.S. (1999). The Nutritional Value of Indigenous Fruits and Vegetables of Sarawak. *Asia Pacific Journal of Clinical Nutrition* 7(3).

Voon, B.H., Sabariah, P., Sim, C.Y.P. & Chin, T.H. (1992). *Wild Fruits and Vegetables in Sarawak*. 2nd ed. Department of Agriculture, Sarawak.

Whitmore, T.C. (1984). *Tropical Rain Forests of the Far East*. 2nd ed. Oxford University Press.

Wong, K.M. (2016). *The Genus Melastoma in Borneo: including 31 new species*. Natural History Publications (Borneo), Kota Kinabalu in association with National Parks Board, Singapore.

Wong, K.M. (2017). *The Genus Saurauia in Borneo*. Natural History Publications (Borneo), Kota Kinabalu in association with National Parks Board, Singapore.

Wong, K.M. & Dransfield, J. (1996). *A Checklist of the Flowering Plants & Gymnosperms of Brunei*. Ministry of Industry and Primary Resources, Bandar Seri Begawan, Brunei.

Wong, K.M., Joffre Ali Ahmad, Low, Y.W & Muhammad Ariffin A. Kalat (2015). *Rainforest Plants and Flowers of Brunei Darussalam*. Forest Department Brunei Darussalam & National Parks Board, Singapore.

Wong, W.W.W. & Lamb, A. (1993). *Fruits, Nuts & Spices*. Department of Agriculture, Sabah.

Wong, W.W.W., Chong, T.C. & Jabi Ternanak (2007). *Fruits of Sabah*, Vol. 1. Department of Agriculture, Sabah.

Acknowledgements

I would like to thank Tan Jiew Hoe (Board Director of Gardens by The Bay, Singapore) for his continued support with the guide books I have been involved in over the last decade.

My great appreciation goes to Datuk C.L. Chan for all his support and publishing of this guide, and in particular to his staff Ms Lo Shiau Yen for all her hard work with the typing out and subsequent corrections of the drafts of the guide, also to Chan Hin Ching for his help with work on plates and Kay Lyons for editing the text.

When I was posted at the Agricultural Research Station at Ulu Dusun which had a large area of lowland rainforest with a rich diversity of wild fruit trees, I sought the help of forest botanists Peter Cockburn and the late Dr Willem Meijer to help identify the various species. As a result of this, I came into contact with many tropical botanists who visited Sabah for field work to identify and collect specimens of orchids and plants in other families, and it was working with these botanists that I picked up much of my present knowledge on the wild fruit trees. In particular, I met up with the late Dr T.C. Whitmore and Dr Peter Ashton, and worked with the late Dr Andre Kostermans and Jean-Marie Bompard on mangoes, Dr Peter van Welzen on the Sapindaceae, Raoul Haegens on the genus *Baccaurea* and Dr John Dransfield on rattan palms, in addition to many other botanists working in other families.

For my past and present field work, I owe thanks to my former Directors and Deputy Directors in the Department of Agriculture in Sabah, especially Datuk Aripin Ampong, and Dr Tay Eng Beok, and Research Agronomist William W.W. Wong, and the present Director of Agriculture, Idrus Shafie, for their support.

For help in access to study and photograph fruit trees in the germplasm collections at the Agricultural Research Station in Tenom, my thanks to the Asst. Director of Research, Jinius Jipanin, fruit tree agronomist Jabi bin Tananak, and his staff, in particular Clarence Matthew, and to Research Officer, Herbert Lim. This help was also given by the Sabah Agriculture Park, Tenom, manager and park botanist Jain Linton, and horticulturist Nurul Syariah, to study and photograph fruit species in the Sabah Agriculture Park and by the Asst. Director of Research, Ms Au Yong Wai Fong, and staff at the Agricultural Research Station, Ulu Dusun, Sandakan to visit and study the fruit trees there.

This guide book would not have been possible without the support of the former Director of the Forest Department Sabah, Datuk Sam Mannan, whilst I was attached to the Forest Research Centre, and the staff at the centre for all their help and assistance: Dr Lee Ying Fah (Former Deputy Conservator of the

ACKNOWLEDGEMENTS

Forest Department), Dr Robert Ong, the present Deputy Conservator for Forest Research and Head of the Natural Forest Section and Rainforest Discovery Centre, together with Dr Reuben Nilus (Forest Ecologist), other staff at the centre, and Jamirus Jumian at the Discovery Garden and Arboretum.

My thanks also to John Sugau, Head of the Herbarium and Systematic Botany at Sepilok, and botanists Dr Joan Pereira and S. Suzana, and staff of the Sandakan Herbarium including the late Ubaldus Majawal, for help with photographs, and Postar Miun with help and information on the native fruits.

I thank Linus Gokusing and Dr Steven Bosuang of Kipandi Park in the Crocker Range, for their help in searching and photographing native fruits.

I thank Julia Sang of the Sarawak Forest Department in my search for information and photographs, and Dr Sri Rahayu at the Bogor Botanic Gardens for information and photographs of fruits in Kalimantan.

In Sarawak, I learnt about the fruits in earlier years when I met Dr Paul Chai and Voon Boon Hoe, and benefited much from them.

In recent years on a field trip I have met up with Prof. Nyree Zarega and Elliot Gardner and received information on their research on the genus *Artocarpus* for which they will be publishing an updated phylogeny.

Belia Emoi kindly provided the drawings for the illustrated glossary of botanical terms.

I must also thank Prof. David Simpson, Dr Andre Schuiteman and Dr Tim Utteridge during my visits to the Herbarium at the Royal Botanic Gardens to study fruit tree specimens from Borneo.

Dr David Middleton and Dr Wong Khoon Meng of the Herbarium at the Singapore Botanic Gardens have provided useful comments and revision of the introduction of this book, and Louise Neo has very kindly made corrections of the text in the species treatment.

Finally I must thank my family for all their support and help: my wife Anthea Phillipps-Lamb, and Serena and Aleaxander Lamb.

Photo Credits

Anthony Lamb: pp. vi, 26, 34, 38, 42, 44, 45, 48–53, 56, 57, 60–65, 67, 72, 74, 80 (left), 81 (inset), 82, 85, 89, 90–94, 98, 99, 101, 104, 105, 110, 111, 117–125, 132, 135 (above), 136, 138, 140, 147 (inset), 152–154, 156, 158, 159, 160 (right), 161, 162, 164–167, 170–172, 174, 175 (inset), 178, 180, 181, 183–186, 188, 189, 191, 192, 194, 195 (inset), 205, 207, 208, 210, 211, 213, 214, 218–220, 224, 225, 234–236, 239–242, 244, 245, 247, 250, 253 (below), 255, 257 (inset), 264 (inset), 266 & 274.

William W.W. Wong: pp. 27, 30 (right), 31, 35 (inset), 39–41, 47, 58, 59, 77, 78, 79, 80 (right), 81, 83, 88, 95, 106, 107, 115, 133, 135 (inset), 137, 141, 160 (left), 187, 203 (above right), 216, 237, 238 (above), 243, 254 (above), 258, 265 (below), 268, 269, 271–273 & 275.

Anthea Phillipps: pp. ix, 68, 96, 108 (right), 116, 123 (inset), 128 (above), 134, 145, 147, 175, 226, 228, 251, 253 (above), 254 (below), 256, 257 & 262–264, 286, 288 & 296.

Rex Yang: pp. 69, 70, 73, 85 (inset left), 111 (inset), 141 (inset), 150, 151, 157, 197, 198 (inset) & 203 (below right).

Linus Gokusing: front cover, pp. 28, 29, 86, 87, 112, 113, 135, 163, 195, 200, 201, 204, 212, 260, 261, 270 & 271 (inset).

Julia Sang: pp. 46, 53 (inset), 66, 76, 102, 103, 114, 142 (inset), 182, 222, 223, 259 & 267.

Roslan Bin Lusi: half-title page, pp. 25, 127, 129 (above), 130, 168, 169 & 177.

Steven Bosuang: pp. 29 (inset), 179 (inset), 227, 230, 231, 232 & 269 (inset).

Jain Linton: pp. 27 (inset), 32, 33, 126, 129 (below), 165 (inset) & 209

Chien Lee: frontispiece, pp. iv, 7, 8, 9, 10, 12, 15, 18, 19, 20, 22, 23, 24, 100, 206, endpaper.

Quentin Phillipps: pp. 146, 148, 149, 161 (inset), 190, 193, 217 & 221.

Postar Miun: pp. 108 (left), 109 & 140 (above).

Ubaldus Majawal: pp. 54, 55 & 84.

Sri Rahayu: pp. 30 (left), 36 (right) & 37.

Herbert Lim: pp. 128 (below) & 179.

Wong Khoon Meng: pp. 196 & 198.

Yao Tze Leong: pp. 202 & 203.

John Sugau: pp. 35 & 43.

Amrafel Marang: p. 238 (below).

C.L. Chan: p. 47 (inset).

Guy Broome: p. x.

Hjh. Hairani binti Ismawi: p. 248.

Jackz Lee: p. 176.

Jimmy Omar: p. 142.

Joe Pan: back cover.

John Beaufoy: p. xii.

Keegan Hickey: p. 89 (inset).

Markus Gumbilil: p. 97.

Miyabi Nakabayashi: p. 246.

Rismita Sari-Reni Lestari: p. 36 (left).

Robert Ong: p. 2.

Saniyatun Maratus Sholihah: p. 249.

Saw Leng Guan: p. 75.

Index to Common Names

A Guide to Wild Fruits of Borneo

A Guide to Wild Fruits of Borneo

Index to Scientific Names